JEPPESEN®

GUIDED FLIGHT DISCOVERY

INSTRUMENT COMMERCIAL SYLLABUS

Jeppesen Sanderson, Inc.

Published in the United States of America
Jeppesen Sanderson, Inc.
55 Inverness Drive East, Englewood, CO 80112-5498
www.jeppesen.com

ISBN-13: 978-0-88487-390-7
ISBN-10: 0-88487-390-0

Jeppesen Sanderson, Inc.
55 Inverness Dr. East
Englewood, CO 80112-5498
Web Site: www.jeppesen.com
Email: Captain@jeppesen.com

Printed in the United States of America

JS344525-008

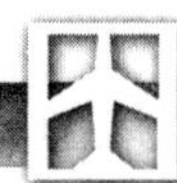

TABLE OF CONTENTS

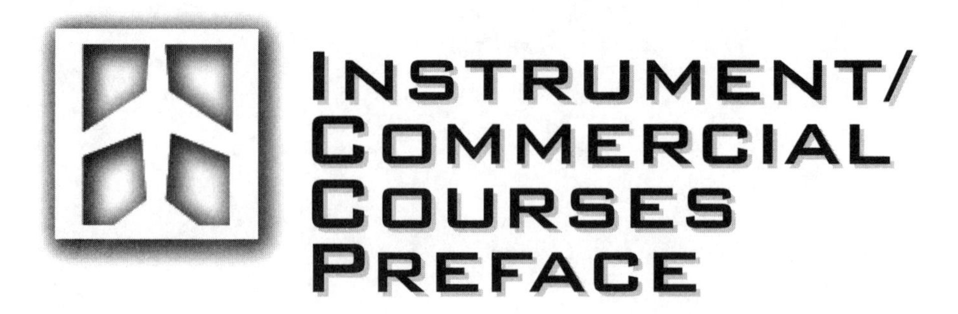

INSTRUMENT/ COMMERCIAL COURSES PREFACE

The *Instrument/Commercial Syllabus* has been specifically developed to meet the requirements of Title 14 CFR, Part 141, Appendicies C, D, and I, which apply to Instrument Rating, Commercial Pilot Certification, and Aircraft Class Rating Courses, respectively. It is important that instructors refer to the pertinent sections of the regulations during the conduct of the course. This will ensure that all aeronautical knowledge areas, flight proficiency, and experience requirements have been included during training and are documented in appropriate records. The terminology for maneuvers and procedures listed in the syllabus is aligned with the "tasks" which are published in applicable FAA Practical Test Standards.

The syllabus is arranged with separate ground and flight training segments which are taught concurrently. The Ground Training Syllabus is divided into five stages. Stages I, II, and III for the instrument rating (airplane), and Stages IV and V are for commercial pilot (airplane single-engine). Stage VI of the Ground Training Syllabus is for the multi-engine rating. The Flight Training Syllabus includes Stages I, II, and III for the instrument rating and Stages IV, V, and VI for commercial pilot (airplane single-engine). Stage VII of the Flight Training Syllabus is for the multi-engine rating.

In concert with long-standing recommendations by both government and the general aviation industry, technological advances, such as computer-aided training, are incorporated into this syllabus. Use of a Personal Computer-Based Aviation Training Device (PCATD) for introductory and skill enhancement purposes is recommended for instrument flight training in the Instrument Rating Course. This syllabus contains provisions for use of a flight simulator or flight training device for instrument flight training. In the Commercial Course, provisions for a multi-engine rating are also included. Operators who wish to utilize these options should check the appropriate box(es) when they apply for Training Course Outline (TCO) approval. The student copy of the syllabus also should be marked accordingly.

- ❑ **This syllabus utilizes a PCATD in the ground and flight training segments of the Instrument Rating Course.**
- ❑ **This syllabus utilizes a flight simulator or a flight training device for the flight training segments of the Instrument Rating Course.**
- ❑ **This syllabus includes a multi-engine rating.**

Students possessing a private pilot certificate who want to obtain a commercial pilot certificate may enroll in the Instrument/Commercial Courses concurrently. Private pilots wanting to pursue only the instrument rating (airplane) may do so by completing Stages I, II, and III of the syllabus. In addition, students who possess a private pilot certificate with an instrument rating may pursue a commercial pilot certificate by completing Flight Stages IV, V, and VI of the syllabus for the single-engine rating and then continuing on through the multi-engine training in Stage VII. Students may begin the appropriate courses provided the school determines they meet the prerequisite knowledge, experience, and proficiency requirements for that rating or certificate.

The stages a student must complete for the various courses are indicated below.

____ is enrolled in the:
(Name)

❑ INSTRUMENT/COMMERCIAL COURSE

The combined Instrument/Commercial Course requires the student to hold a private pilot certificate and be concurrently enrolled in the Instrument Rating Course and the Commercial Pilot Certification Course. The student must complete all of the ground training lessons in Stages I through V and all of the flight training lessons in Stages I through VI in the *Instrument/Commercial Syllabus.*

❑ INSTRUMENT RATING COURSE

The student must hold a private pilot certificate and complete all of the instrument ground and flight training lessons in Stages I, II, and III of the *Instrument/Commercial Syllabus.*

❑ COMMERCIAL PILOT CERTIFICATION COURSE

The student must hold a private pilot certificate with an instrument rating and complete all of the ground training lessons in Stages IV, and V and all of the flight training lessons in Stages IV, V, and VI of the Instrument/Commercial Syllabus.

INTRODUCTION

The Instrument/Commercial Courses contain coordinated ground and flight training lessons. They follow a careful, step-by-step progression of subject introduction and practice, incorporating academic assignments, the training aircraft, and flight simulation devices where appropriate. The structure of the syllabus is not overly complex, but it does require a thorough understanding on the part of the instructor if maximum benefit is to be realized. When the principles and general order of the syllabus are followed, they make the difference between an effective program or a succession of lessons that lack order and direction. However, even though the ground and flight lessons are coordinated and arranged in a logical sequence, the syllabus should not be considered a rigid document. Any syllabus should be considered as an abstract or digest of the course of training. As such, it is important that flexibility be provided to adapt to individual student needs and/or the local training environment.

COURSE ELEMENTS

The *Instrument/Commercial Syllabus* utilizes separate ground and flight segments. It may be conducted as a combined ground and flight training program, or it may be divided into separate components. Regardless of the method used, the course includes the latest FAA pilot certification requirements and a maximum of student-oriented instruction. The syllabus and support materials not only provide necessary information, but also guide the student through the course in a logical manner.

The basic syllabus is designed for the instrument rating (airplane) and the commercial certificate (airplane single-engine). However, additional ground training (Stage VI) and flight training (Stage VII) is included to add a multi-engine rating to your commercial certificate. Applicants may complete only the single-engine stages, or they may continue through the multi-engine training. In either case, at completion, the applicant will have complied with the training requirements of 14 CFR Part 141, Appendix C, Appendix D, and Appendix I.

GROUND TRAINING

In accordance with FAR Part 141, ground school training is an integral part of pilot certification courses. The Ground Training Syllabus has been designed to meet this requirement, and it may be coordinated with the Flight Training Syllabus or used as a separate ground training course.

If the ground school is coordinated with the flight syllabus, each ground lesson is conducted at the point indicated in the Lesson Time Allocation tables. This is the most effective method for course utilization, because the academic knowledge is obtained immediately prior to its application during flight training. However, to provide a degree of flexibility for adapting to individual student needs and the training environment, the syllabus lesson and stages may be altered with approval of the chief flight instructor. Any deviation should not disturb the course continuity or objective.

When the course is presented as a formal classroom program, lessons should be followed as outlined. Each lesson may be presented in one classroom session, or it may be divided into two or more sessions, as necessary.

GROUND LESSONS

The ground lessons generally are divided into three elements — Lesson Introduction, Video Presentation, and Class Discussion. During the Lesson Introduction, the instructor should outline the subject material to be covered, the objective for learning that information, and the performance standards necessary for successful lesson completion.

TEXTBOOKS

Prior to each ground lesson, the student should read and study the assigned textbook section or chapter, if appropriate. The *Instrument/Commercial* textbook is the main source of information for the first five stages of ground training. It is comprehensive and well illustrated. The *Multi-Engine* textbook covers information necessary to complete the multi-engine stage of training. In addition, the FAR/AIM contains information essential for course completion.

DVD PRESENTATIONS

Selected lessons include video presentations from the Instrument/Commercial Video Course which are viewed after the lesson introduction. These presentations include subjects specifically designed for the Instrument/Commercial Course. In addition, the Multi-Engine Video Course is assigned for the multi-engine option. Schools that have access to the Private Video Course may assign additional videos to compliment appropriate ground lessons. These additional video presentations can be credited toward meeting the ground training time requirements.

SOFTWARE

The instrument knowledge areas also are covered in the FliteSchool CD-ROMs. These computer-based, multimedia software programs are organized into easy-to-study lessons that correspond to the chapters and sections in the *Instrument/Commercial* textbook; they provide an additional resource for study and review. FliteSchool offers an alternative study method to accomodate individual needs and learning styles. Since FliteSchool is primarily intended for self-study, its use is recommended, but not required. Another training tool is the Jeppesen FliteStar flight planning software. An orientation on use of this software may be included in conjunction with IFR cross-country flight planning during the last stage of instrument training.

EXERCISE QUESTIONS AND STAGE EXAMS

The final step is for the student to complete the appropriate quiz or textbook exercise questions and discuss any incorrect responses with the instructor. This ensures student understanding prior to beginning the next ground lesson. When the lesson is complete, the instructor assigns the next textbook section or chapter for out-of-class reading. At the end of each stage, the student is required to successfully complete the stage exam outlined in the syllabus before the next ground training stage.

END-OF-COURSE EXAMS

When all the appropriate ground lesson assignments are complete, the student should take the end-of-course exam. The ground lesson assignments for the Instrument Rating End-of-Course Exam are completed in Stage III, and those for the Commercial Pilot (Airplane Single-Engine) End-of-Course Exam are completed in Stage V.

The ground training end-of-course exam for the combined Instrument/Commercial Course (Airplane Single-Engine) is administered following Stage V. The Commercial Pilot End-of-Course Exam serves as this final test. An additional end-of-course exam is also included for students completing the multi-engine rating. Following these tests, the instructor should assign each student appropriate subject areas for review.

PILOT BRIEFINGS

The pilot briefings are found in the *Instructor's Guide* CD. Each briefing consists of a series of questions which provide comprehensive coverage of selected areas of instruction. The student should be provided with the appropriate briefing in advance. This allows the student to prepare properly by researching the answers and, therefore, gain optimum benefit from the briefing.

The briefings should be conducted as private tutoring sessions to test each student's comprehension. Every question should be discussed thoroughly to ensure the student understands the relevant information. The briefings are to be completed during the preflight orientation for the appropriate flight. Correct placement of the briefing sessions is indicated in the syllabus.

Altogether there are seven pilot briefings in the Instrument/Commercial Course (Airplane Single-Engine). The third one is the briefing for the Instrument Rating Practical Test. It should be completed prior to the end-of-course flight check in Stage III. The seventh briefing is for the Commercial Course (Airplane Single-Engine) and it should be completed before the single-engine end-of-course flight check in Stage VI. Additional pilot briefings are included in the airplane multi-engine stage. During all of the pilot briefings, each subject area should be reviewed with the student to ensure complete understanding.

FLIGHT TRAINING

As indicated earlier, the syllabus is divided into three stages for the instrument rating portion of the course and an additional three stages to complete the commercial portion. Each stage builds on previous learning and, therefore, it is recommended they be completed in sequence.

Since the *Instrument/Commercial Syllabus* is to be used as a practical training guide, it is designed to allow a degree of flexibility in order to meet the needs of individual students. With the approval of the chief flight instructor, some lessons may be rearranged to suit training needs. However, it is the responsibility of the instructor to ensure the continuity of the learning blocks remains unaffected by the change. The following discussion presents a description of the primary areas of study in each stage.

STAGE I

Stage I of the syllabus is designed to provide the student with a strong foundation in attitude instrument flight and instrument navigation. At the completion of this stage, the student is thoroughly prepared for the introduction of holding patterns and instrument approach procedures.

STAGE II

During this stage, the student learns to perform holding patterns and instrument approaches. This training prepares the student for the introduction of IFR enroute procedures in Stage III.

STAGE III

This stage of training teaches the student IFR enroute procedures and provides a review of all previously learned maneuvers. Through the use of three instrument cross-country flights and review, the student is able to attain the proficiency level of an instrument-rated pilot.

The ground and flight training portions of the instrument course are completed in Stage III. The student should also successfully pass the FAA instrument rating airmen knowledge test and take the FAA instrument rating practical test at the completion of this stage.

STAGE IV

Stage IV builds upon previously learned ground and flight training. The student will review and practice day and night VFR cross-country procedures in preparation for commercial pilot operations.

STAGE V

Stage V provides a thorough introduction and pilot-in-command checkout in the complex airplane. The remainder of the stage is devoted to the introduction and review of precision flight maneuvers.

STAGE VI

Although no new maneuvers or procedures are introduced in Stage VI, practice of commercial maneuvers in the complex aircraft is included. This is an important stage of training. It provides a review of the skills learned throughout the syllabus and prepares the student for the FAA practical test. If the student has not previously completed the instrument rating practical test, both the Instrument and Commercial Flight Test Oral Preparation Briefings that coincide with the end-of-course flight check are to be utilized in this stage.

STAGE VII

Stage VII, which is for the multi-engine rating, provides a foundation for all relevant multi-engine maneuvers and procedures, including normal and engine-out operations. The final portion of Stage VII concentrates on multi-engine procedures in the IFR environment with both normal instrument approaches and engine-out instrument approach procedures.

PREFLIGHT ORIENTATION

Prior to each dual and solo flight, the instructor must provide the student with an overview of the subject matter to be covered during the lesson. The instructor should brief the student and explain the lesson objectives and completion standards. It is important that the instructor define unfamiliar terms and explain the maneuvers and procedures of each lesson. The preflight orientation should be tailored to the specific flight, the local environment, and the individual student. Proper preparation of the student also applies to flight lessons involving use of a simulator, FTD, or PCATD.

AIRPLANE PRACTICE

The syllabus has been constructed to allow practice of given procedures and maneuvers after the student has been introduced to the maneuver by the instructor. If a flight simulation device is used, the instructor is not relieved of teaching during flight lessons. However, the student is expected to grasp new techniques more easily having already been introduced to them in the simulation device. If simulation devices are not utilized, both introduction and practice are to be accomplished in the airplane.

USE OF PERSONAL COMPUTER-BASED AVIATION TRAINING DEVICE (PCATD)

The syllabus provides for use of a personal computer-based aviation training device (PCATD) to enhance training for the instrument course. A PCATD determined to meet the established criteria of AC 61-126, *Qualification and Approval of PCATDs*, may be used for 10 hours of the instrument training time that ordinarily would be acquired in an airplane. The PCATD will improve the applicant's knowledge and understanding of instrument procedures.

In addition to knowledge enhancement, the introduction of maneuvers and procedures by instrument reference in the PCATD has other advantages for both student and instructor. These include fewer distractions, more versatility in lesson presentation, repositioning, freeze functions, emergency training, and the ability to control the environment of the training session and allow the student to concentrate on the areas the instructor wants to emphasize.

Instructor-directed PCATD training includes 10 hours of flight training. Table 1 lists the dual flight lessons where an approved PCATD may be used for the Instrument Rating Course. Placement of these lessons is indicated in the Lesson Time Allocation tables and in the flight training portion of the syllabus. In addition, PCATD training is included as part of selected ground lessons. This is indicated in the Lesson Time Allocation tables and in the individual ground lessons. Because of the advantages of this type of training, use of the PCATD by students for extra, unsupervised PCATD training is encouraged. Additional information on use of the PCATD is included in the *Instructor's Guide* CD.

If a PCATD is not available, a flight training device (FTD) that is representative of the training aircraft for which the course is approved may be used in lieu of the PCATD. A training airplane for which the course is approved also may be used in lieu of the PCATD or FTD.

FLIGHT LESSONS APPROPRIATE FOR USE OF A PCATD					
STAGE I		STAGE II		STAGE III	
Flight	Time	Flight	Time	Flight	Time
2	1.0	14	1.0	24	1.0
4	1.0	18	1.0		
8	1.0	19	1.0		
10	1.0	20	1.0		
		22	1.0		

Table 1

FLIGHT SIMULATOR/FLIGHT TRAINING DEVICE

If the flight school incorporates the use of a flight simulator or FTD in the advanced training program, the syllabus allows for the introduction of new material and procedural review in these training aids. If the school possesses a flight simulator meeting the requirements of FAR 141.41(a), up to a maximum of 50 percent of the flight training hour requirements for the Instrument Rating and 30 percent of the total flight training hour requirements for the Commercial Pilot Certification Course may be in the simulator. If the school possesses an FTD meeting the requirements of FAR 141.41(b), the training time may be reduced up to 40 percent of the flight training hour requirements for the Instrument Rating Course and 20 percent of the total flight training hour requirements for the Commercial Pilot Certification course. Table 2 lists the dual flights where an approved simulator or flight training device may be used for the Instrument Rating Course. Operators may designate additional lessons from the commercial segment of the course if they desire. In the event a flight simulator or FTD is not available, a training aircraft for which the course is approved may be used.

FLIGHT LESSONS APPROPRIATE FOR USE OF A SIMULATOR OR FTD			
Flight			
2	1.0	14	1.0
3	1.0	15	1.0
4	1.0	16	1.5
6	1.0	17	1.0
7	1.0	18	1.0
8	1.0	19	1.0
9	1.0	20	1.0
10	1.0	22	1.0
		24	1.0

Table 2

POSTFLIGHT EVALUATION

The postflight evaluation is as important as the preflight orientation. During each postflight session, the student should be debriefed thoroughly. Noticeable advancement should be apparent and, where appropriate, recommendations should be made for improvement. This action is a valuable instructional technique because it increases retention and, to some degree, prepares the student for the next lesson.

Preflight orientation and postflight evaluation times are listed as required in the course time tables. This provides flexibility for dealing with individual students.

STUDENT STAGE CHECKS

The stage checks in the *Instrument/Commercial Syllabus* are designed to identify deficiencies and to check the student's overall progress in accordance with FAR Part 141. Each stage check is the responsibility of the chief flight instructor. However, the chief flight instructor may delegate the authority to conduct these tests to the assistant chief instructor or designated check instructor. This procedure provides close supervision of training and a second opinion on the student's progress. The stage check also gives the chief instructor an opportunity to check the effectiveness of the instructors and their teaching methods.

An examination of the building-block theory of learning will show that it is extremely important that the student's progress and proficiency are satisfactory before entering a new stage of training. Therefore, the next stage should not begin until the student successfully completes the stage check. Failure to follow this progression may defeat the purpose of the stage check and lead to overall course breakdown.

IMPLEMENTING THE COURSE

While the *Instrument/Commercial Syllabus* is intended to fulfill the requirements of a combined Instrument/Commercial Course, it may also be utilized for separate Instrument Rating or Commercial Pilot Certification Courses. This discussion explains the implementation of the combined Instrument/Commercial, as well as the separate Instrument Rating, and separate Commercial Pilot Certification Courses.

CREDIT FOR PREVIOUS TRAINING

According to FAR 141.77(c), when a student transfers from one FAA-approved school to another approved school, course credits obtained in the previous course of training may be credited for 50 percent of the curriculum requirements by the receiving school. However, the receiving school must determine the amount of credits to be allowed based upon a proficiency test, knowledge test, or both, conducted by the receiving school. A student who enrolls in a course of training may receive credit for 25 percent of the curriculum requirements for knowledge and experience gained in a Part 61 flight school, and the credit must be based upon a proficiency test, knowledge test, or both, conducted by the receiving school. The amount of credit for previous training allowed, whether received from an FAA-approved school or other source, is determined by the receiving school. In addition, the previous provider of the training must certify the kind and amount of training given, and the result of each stage check and end-of-course test, if applicable.

INSTRUMENT/ COMMERCIAL COURSE

The Instrument/Commercial Course is designed for students who currently hold a private pilot certificate. The course includes a total of at least 65 hours of ground training and 155 hours of flight training. This total consists of 30 hours of ground training and 35 hours of flight training in Stages I, II, and III of the syllabus for the instrument rating segment. In addition, the commercial certification segment consists of 35 hours of ground training and 120 hours of flight training found in Stages IV, V, and VI.

An additional stage of flight training, Stage VII, is provided for students seeking a multi-engine rating. Extra ground training in Stage VI of the ground training syllabus also is included for these students.

The *Instrument/Commercial Syllabus* is presented in both an overview and a lesson-by-lesson format. The combined course includes the entire outline from Stage I through the completion of Stage VII. The lesson sequence and content have been designed to provide the student with maximum academic and flight training prior to the introduction of new maneuvers or procedures. Therefore, the sequence of ground and fight training shown in the syllabus outline should not be altered significantly if the coordinated program is utilized.

If absolutely necessary, the placement of ground lesson assignments may be changed to allow the student to progress more rapidly in the academic study than outlined in the course. If this method is used, the student should not be allowed to progress into the ground lesson assignments of the next stage until the flight lessons in the current stage of training are completed. This is important, because the student's recall of academic knowledge decreases with an increase in time between subject introduction during ground training and its application in flight training.

INSTRUMENT RATING COURSE

The Instrument Rating Course is presented first in the *Instrument/Commercial Syllabus.* It consists of a minimum of 30 hours of ground training and 35 hours of instrument flight training in Stages I, II, and III of the syllabus. During Stage III the student should pass the FAA instrument rating airmen knowledge test. At the completion of Stage III, the FAA instrument rating practical test should be taken.

The *Instrument Rating Syllabus* is presented in both an overview and a lesson-by-lesson format. The combined flight and ground training course includes the entire outline from Stage I through the completion of Stage III. The lesson sequence and content have been designed to provide the student with maximum academic and flight training prior to the introduction of new maneuvers and procedures. However, the sequence shown in the syllabus outline may be altered to meet special circumstances of the student or training environment.

NOTE: *Operators utilizing the PCATD option in the Instrument/Commercial or Instrument Rating Course may credit up to 10 hours of PCATD time toward flight training and up to 5 hours toward ground training requirements.*

COMMERCIAL PILOT CERTIFICATION COURSE

The Commercial Pilot Certification Course is presented in the next segment of the *Instrument/Commercial Syllabus.* It consists of a minimum of 35 hours of ground training and 120 hours of flight training in Stages IV, V, and VI. During Stage V, the student should pass the FAA commercial pilot airmen knowledge test. At the completion of Stage VI, the FAA commercial pilot practical test should be taken by students not enrolled in the multi-engine portion. Those enrolled in the multi-engine segment must complete Ground Stage VI and Flight Stage VII. An additional 14 hours of ground training is included in Ground Stage VI for the multi-engine rating.

The *Commercial Pilot Syllabus* is presented in both an overview and a lesson-by-lesson format. The combined flight and ground training course includes the entire outline from Stage IV through the completion of Stage VI, plus the multi-engine rating in Stage VII. The lesson sequence and content have been designed to provide the student with maximum academic and flight training prior to the introduction of new maneuvers and procedures. While the syllabus provides a general training outline, the lesson sequence shown may be tailored to meet the individual needs of the student. Lessons 36, 37, 38, 39, 40 and 41 are designed to be solo cross-country flight lessons. However, these lessons may also be utilized for additional dual instruction to meet the proficiency requirements for the end-of-course flight check and FAA practical test.

FAR PART 61 TRAINING

The *Instrument/Commercial Syllabus* is designed to meet all of the requirements of FAR Part 141, Appendices, C, D, and I. It may also be adapted to meet the requirements of FAR Part 61. FAR Part 61 incorporates greater aeronautical experience requirements than are found in FAR Part 141. For example, as indicated in FAR 61.65 for an instrument rating, you must have at least 50 hours of cross-country time as pilot in command and 40 hours of actual or simulated instrument time in the areas of operation specified in the FARs. This includes at least 15 hours of instrument flight training from an authorized instructor in the aircraft category for which the instrument rating is sought. If your training is accomplished under FAR Part 141, you must have 35 hours of instrument training from an authorized instructor in the areas specified in Appendix C, FAR Part 141 and need not comply with the 50-hour PIC cross-country requirement.

Under FAR Part 61, a commercial pilot applicant for an airplane category and single-engine class rating must log at least 250 hours of flight time as a pilot. This includes 100 hours in powered aircraft, of which 50 hours must be in airplanes. In addition, it must include 100 hours of pilot-in-command time, which includes at least 50 hours in cross-country flight of which at least 10 hours must be in airplanes. Further, 20 hours of flight training and 10 hours of solo flight also are required. Refer to FAR 61.125, 61.127, and 61.129.

Under FAR Part 61, an applicant for a multi-engine class rating to be added to a pilot certificate must meet the requirements of FAR 61.63 (c). Essentially, there are no established minimum amounts of ground training or flight training time necessary in order to add an additional aircraft class rating to a pilot certificate. As a result, class ratings are often referred to as competency-based. FAR Part 61 requires instruction be received appropriate to the desired rating, and that a flight instructor recommendation be obtained. Of course the appropriate practical test also must be successfully completed. The ground training requirements under FAR Part 61 specify that an applicant for a knowledge test is required to have a logbook endorsement from an authorized instructor who conducted the training or reviewed the person's home study course. The endorsement must indicate satisfactory completion of the ground instruction or home study course required for the certificate or rating sought.

However, an applicant who applies for an additional class rating to be added on a pilot certificate need not take an additional knowledge test, provided the applicant holds an airplane, rotorcraft, powered-lift, or airship rating at that pilot certificate level. A home study course for the purposes of FAR Part 61 is a course of study in those aeronautical knowledge areas specified in FAR 61.125, and organized by a pilot school, publisher, flight or ground instructor, or by the student. The Instrument/Commercial Course easily meets this requirement. As a practical consideration, students seeking pilot certification under FAR Part 61 should receive some formal ground training, either in the classroom or from an authorized flight or ground instructor.

CURRICULUM OVERVIEW

INTRODUCTION

The *Instrument/Commercial Syllabus* is designed to coordinate the academic study assignments and flight training required by pilots operating in an increasingly complex aviation environment. New subject matter is introduced during the ground lessons, which include five items:

1. In-depth textbook assignments
2. Video presentations
3. Thorough instructor/student discussions
4. Exercise questions
5. Stage and end-of-course exams for evaluation and reinforcement

After completing the ground lesson, the student will apply these new principles in a simulation device or in the airplane during the flight lesson. The Lesson Time Allocation tables indicate placement of the ground lessons when the coordinated sequence is used.

Optimum effectiveness is realized when ground lessons are completed just prior to the respective flight lessons, as outlined in the syllabus. However, it is also acceptable to present lessons in a formal ground school before the student is introduced to the airplane. If a considerable length of time has elapsed between the ground lesson and the associated flight, the instructor may wish to conduct a short review of essential material. Flight lessons should not be conducted until related ground lessons have been completed.

INSTRUMENT RATING COURSE

COURSE OBJECTIVE — The student will obtain the knowledge, skill, and aeronautical experience necessary to meet the requirements for an instrument rating (airplane).

COURSE COMPLETION STANDARD — The student must demonstrate through knowledge tests, flight tests, and show through appropriate records that he/she meets the knowledge, skill, and experience requirements necessary to obtain an instrument rating (airplane).

FLIGHT TRAINING COURSE OBJECTIVE — The student will obtain the aeronautical skill and experience necessary to meet the requirements for an instrument rating (airplane).

COMPLETION STANDARD — The student must demonstrate through flight tests and school records that the necessary aeronautical skill and experience requirements to obtain an instrument rating (airplane) have been met.

GROUND TRAINING COURSE OBJECTIVE — The student will obtain the necessary aeronautical knowledge and meet the prerequisites specified in FAR Part 141 for the instrument rating airmen knowledge test.

COMPLETION STANDARD — The student has demonstrated through practical and knowledge tests, and records, that he/she meets the prerequisites specified in FAR Part 141 and has the knowledge necessary to pass the instrument rating airmen knowledge test.

STUDENT INFORMATION

COURSE ENROLLMENT

To enroll in the flight portion of the Instrument Rating Course, you must hold at least a private pilot certificate with an airplane category rating and a single-engine land class rating.

REQUIREMENTS FOR GRADUATION

To obtain an instrument rating, you must be able to read, speak, write, and understand the English language and hold a private pilot certificate with at least a third-class medical certificate. In addition, you must meet the aeronautical experience requirements specified in FAR Part 141, Appendix C. When you meet the minimum requirements of FAR Part 141, Appendix C, you may be considered eligible for graduation.

LESSON DESCRIPTION AND STAGES OF TRAINING

Each lesson is fully described within the syllabus, including the objectives, standards, and measurable units of accomplishment and learning for each lesson. The objectives and standards of each stage are described within the syllabus.

TESTS AND CHECKS

The syllabus incorporates stage and end-of-course flight checks in accordance with FAR Part 141, Appendix C. These checks are given by the chief instructor, an assistant chief instructor, or check instructor designated by the chief instructor. You will also complete the appropriate stage exams, pilot briefings, and end-of-course examinations that are described within the syllabus. In addition, you must satisfactorily accomplish a final flight test after all of the stages have been completed in accordance with Part 141, Appendix C.

Note: *This syllabus content supports instrument training aircraft with conventional flight instruments such as attitude indicator, airspeed indicator, altimeter, turn coordinator, vertical speed indicator, and magnetic compass. While this syllabus content supports the latest Instrument Rating PTS, it does not provide for initial instrument training in technically advanced aircraft with electronic flight instrument displays. Refer to the FAA Industry Training Standards (FITS) Master Instructor Syllabus for transition training in technically advanced aircraft.*

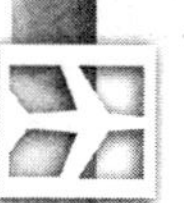

CURRICULUM OVERVIEW
INSTRUMENT RATING COURSE

Completion of this course is based solely upon compliance with the minimum requirements of FAR Part 141. The accompanying time tables are provided for guidance in achieving regulatory compliance.

	GROUND TRAINING			
	Video and Class Discussion	PCATD	Briefings, Stage, and Final Exams	Ground Training Totals
STAGE I	8.0	(2.0)	1.0	9.0
STAGE II	10.0	(3.0)	1.5	11.5
STAGE III	6.0		3.5	9.5
TOTALS	24.0	(5.0)	6.0	30.0

	FLIGHT TRAINING		
	Airplane	PCATD	Flight Training Totals
STAGE I	13.0	(4.0)	13.0
STAGE II	11.0	(5.0)	11.0
STAGE III	11.0	(1.0)	11.0
TOTALS	35.0	(10.0)	35.0

NOTE: 1. All flight training in the *Instrument Rating Course* is dual.
2. Up to 5 hours of PCATD time may be credited toward ground training requirements.
3. Time listed for PCATD in flight training indicates use of the PCATD instead of the airplane for students utilizing the PCATD option. The affected flight lessons are indicated in the Lesson Time Allocation tables and in the individual flight lessons. If the PCATD is not used, times indicated for airplane apply.

COMMERCIAL PILOT CERTIFICATION COURSE

COURSE OBJECTIVE — The student will obtain the knowledge, skill, and aeronautical experience necessary to meet the requirements for a commercial pilot certificate with an airplane category rating and a single-engine land class rating.

COURSE COMPLETION STANDARD — The student must demonstrate through knowledge tests, flight tests, and show through appropriate records that he/she meets the knowledge, skill, and experience requirements necessary to obtain a commercial pilot certificate with an airplane category rating and a single-engine land class rating.

FLIGHT TRAINING COURSE OBJECTIVE — The student will obtain the aeronautical skill and experience necessary to meet the requirements for a commercial pilot certificate with an airplane category rating and a single-engine land class rating.

COMPLETION STANDARD — The student must demonstrate through flight tests and school records that the necessary aeronautical skill and experience requirements to obtain a commercial pilot certificate with an airplane category rating and a single-engine land class rating have been met.

GROUND TRAINING COURSE OBJECTIVE — The student will obtain the necessary aeronautical knowledge and meet the prerequisites specified in FAR Part 141 for the commercial pilot airmen knowledge test.

COMPLETION STANDARD — The student has demonstrated through practical and knowledge tests, and records, that he/she meets the prerequisites specified in FAR Part 141 and has the aeronautical knowledge necessary to pass the commercial pilot airmen knowledge test.

STUDENT INFORMATION

COURSE ENROLLMENT

To enroll in the flight portion of the Commercial Pilot Certification Course, you must hold at least a private pilot certificate. In addition, you must hold an instrument rating or be concurrently enrolled in an instrument rating (airplane) course.

REQUIREMENTS FOR GRADUATION

To obtain a commercial pilot certificate, you must be able to read, speak, write, and understand the English language. In addition, you must have a valid FAA third-class medical certificate. However, to exercise the privileges of a commercial pilot you must possess a valid second-class medical certificate. When you meet the minimum requirements of FAR Part 141, Appendix D, you may be considered eligible for graduation. In addition, you must be at least 18 years of age to be eligible for the commercial pilot certificate.

LESSON DESCRIPTION AND STAGES OF TRAINING

Each lesson is fully described within the syllabus, including the learning objectives and standards for each lesson. The objectives and standards of each stage are described within the syllabus.

TESTS AND CHECKS

The syllabus incorporates stage and end-of-course flight checks in accordance with FAR Part 141, Appendix D. These checks are given by the chief instructor, an assistant chief instructor, or check instructor designated by the chief instructor. You will also complete the appropriate stage exams, pilot briefings, and end-of-course examinations that are described within the syllabus. In addition, you must satisfactorily accomplish a final flight test after all of the stages have been completed in accordance with FAR Part 141, Appendix D.

CURRICULUM OVERVIEW
COMMERCIAL PILOT CERTIFICATION COURSE

Completion of this course is based solely upon compliance with the minimum requirements of FAR Part 141. The following time tables are provided only for guidance in achieving regulatory compliance.

GROUND TRAINING

		Video, Class Discussion	Stage and End-of-Course Exams	Briefings/ Debriefings	Ground Training Totals
	STAGE IV	9.0	1.0	As Required	10.0
	STAGE V	22.0	3.0	As Required	25.0
COMM'L SINGLE ENGINE →	TOTALS	31.0	4.0	As Required	35.0
MULTI-ENGINE →	STAGE VI	8.0	2.0	4.0	14.0

FLIGHT TRAINING

		DUAL							SOLO				
		Day Local	Day Cross X-C	Night	Complex	Multi-Engine	Instru-ment	Dual Stage Totals	Day Local	Day Cross X-C	Night	Solo Stage Totals	Dual/ Solo Comb. Totals
	STAGE IV		8.0 (8.0)	5.0 (5.0)			As Required	13.0 (13.0)		34.0*	6.0	40.0	53.0 (53.0)
	STAGE V	20.0 (14.0)			10.0 (7.0)		As Required	20.0 (14.0)	9.0			9.0	29.0 (23.0)
	STAGE VI	20.0 (12.0)	2.0 (1.0)		5.0 (3.0)		As Required	22.0 (13.0)	16.0			16.0	38.0 (29.0)
SINGLE ENGINE →	TOTALS	40.0 (26.0)	10.0 (9.0)	5.0 (5.0)	15.0 (10.0)		As Required	55.0 (40.0)	25.0	34.0*	6.0	65.0	120.0 (105.0)
MULTI-ENGINE →	STAGE VII	(9.0)	(3.0)	(3.0)		(15.0)	As Required	(15.0)					(15.0)
COMBINED →	TOTALS	40.0 (35.0)	10.0 (12.0)	5.0 (8.0)	15.0 (10.0)	(15.0)	As Required	55.0 (55.0)	25.0	34.0*	6.0		120.0 (120.0)

NOTE:
1. * Indicates some solo cross-country hours may be utilized for additional dual instruction to meet the proficiency requirements for the end-of-course flight check and FAA practical test.
2. In blocks where two times are shown, the first time is for students in the standard commercial course without multi-engine training, and the figures in parentheses indicate the minimum time for students who are using the multi-engine option. For example, the dual time totals for Stages IV, V, and VI are 55.0 hours for students not completing the multi-engine training and 40.0 hours for those who will complete the remaining 15 hours in the multi-engine airplane during flight Stage VII. In each case, the student will receive a minimum of 55.0 hours dual.
3. The 15.0 hours in Stage VII are all dual instruction in the multi-engine airplane.

LESSON TIME ALLOCATION

Ground Training						Flight Training							
						Dual						Solo	
Video, Class Discussion	PCATD	Pilot Briefings	Stage/Final Exams	Exam Debriefings		PCATD	Airplane	Day Cross-Country	Night Local	Night Cross-Country	Instrument	Day Local	Day Cross-Country
					STAGE I								
1.0					GL 1 – Training/Opportunities/Human Factors								
1.0					GL 2 – Flight Instrument Systems								
1.0	As Req.				GL 3 – Attitude Instrument Flying								
					FL 1 – Preflight Procedures and Full Panel		1.0				1.0		
					FL 2 – Full Panel and IFR Systems	(1.0)	1.0				1.0		
1.0	As Req.				GL 4 – Instrument Navigation								
					FL 3 – Review Full Panel		1.0				1.0		
					FL 4 – Introduction to Partial Panel	(1.0)	1.0				1.0		
1.0					GL 5 – Instrument FARs								
1.0					GL 6 – Airports, Airspace, and Flight Information								
					FL 5 – Systems and Equipment Malfunctions		1.0				1.0		
					FL 6 – Full and Partial Panel		1.0				1.0		
1.0					GL 7 – ATC System								
					FL 7 – Review		1.0				1.0		
1.0					GL 8 – ATC Clearances								
					FL 8 – VOR Orientation	(1.0)	1.0				1.0		
			1.0	As Req.	GL 9 – Stage I Exam								
					FL 9 – VOR Navigation		1.0				1.0		
					FL 10 – NDB Orientation	(1.0)	1.0				1.0		
					FL 11 – Localizer Tracking		1.0				1.0		
					FL 12 – VOR/NDB Tracking		1.0				1.0		
					FL 13 – Stage Check		1.0				1.0		
8.0	As Req.		1.0	As Req.	Stage Totals	(4.0)	13.0				13.0		

NOTE: 1. The PCATD may be used as required in the ground training lessons indicated.
2. Time listed for PCATD in flight training indicates use of the PCATD instead of the airplane for students utilizing the PCATD option.
3. The individual times shown on the Lesson Time Allocation tables are for instructor/student guidance only; they are not mandatory for each flight, ground lesson, or stage of training. At the completion of this course, the student must meet the minimum requirements of FAR Part 141, for each category in order to graduate. Preflight and postflight briefings are as required.

LESSON TIME ALLOCATION

Ground Training						Flight Training							
						Dual						Solo	
Video, Class Discussion	PCATD	Pilot Briefings	Stage/Final Exams	Exam Debriefings		PCATD	Airplane	Day Cross-Country	Night Local	Night Cross-Country	Instrument	Day Local	Day Cross-Country
					STAGE II								
1.0					GL 10 – Departure Charts and Procedures								
1.5					GL 11 – Enroute Charts and Procedures								
1.0	As Req.				GL 12 – Holding								
					FL 14 – VOR/NDB Holding (Standard)	(1.0)	1.0				1.0		
					FL 15 – VOR/NDB Holding (Nonstandard)		1.0				1.0		
					FL 16 – Localizer/Intersection Holding		1.5				1.5		
1.0					GL 13 – Arrival Charts and Procedures								
1.5					GL 14 – Approach Charts								
1.0					GL 15 – Approach Procedures								
1.0	As Req.				GL 16 – VOR and NDB Approaches								
		.5			Briefing – Introduction to Approaches								
					FL 17 – VOR Approaches		1.0				1.0		
					FL 18 and 19 – VOR and NDB Approaches	(2.0)	2.0				2.0		
1.0	As Req.				GL 17 – ILS Approaches								
					FL 20 – ILS Approaches	(1.0)	1.0				1.0		
					FL 21 – Partial Panel Approaches		1.0				1.0		
1.0					GL 18 – RNAV Approaches								
					FL 22 – Review Holding and Approaches	(1.0)	1.0				1.0		
			1.0	As Req.	GL 19 – Stage II Exam								
					FL 23 – Stage Check		1.5				1.5		
10.0	As Req.	.5	1.0	As Req.	Stage Totals	(5.0)	11.0				11.0		

NOTE: 1. The PCATD may be used as required in the ground training lessons indicated.
2. Time listed for PCATD in flight training indicates use of the PCATD instead of the airplane for students utilizing the PCATD option.

LESSON TIME ALLOCATION

Ground Training						Flight Training							
						Dual						Solo	
Video, Class Discussion	PCATD	Pilot Briefings	Stage/Final Exams	Exam Debriefings		PCATD	Airplane	Day Cross-Country	Night Local	Night Cross-Country	Instrument	Day Local	Day Cross-Country
STAGE III													
1.0					GL 20 – Weather Factors and Hazards								
1.0					GL 21 – Printed Reports and Forecasts								
		.5			Briefing – IFR Cross-Country								
					FL 24 – IFR Cross-Country Procedures	(1.0)	1.0	1.0			1.0		
1.0					GL 22 – Graphic Weather Products								
					FL 25 – IFR Cross-Country		2.0	2.0			2.0		
1.0					GL 23 – Sources of Weather Information								
1.0					GL 24 – IFR Emergencies								
1.0					GL 25 – IFR Decision Making/Flight Planning								
					FL 26 – Long IFR Cross-Country		3.0	3.0			3.0		
		1.0			Briefing – Instrument Rating Practical Test								
					FL 27 – IFR Cross-Country Review		2.0	2.0			2.0		
			1.0	As Req.	GL 26 – Stage III Exam								
					FL 28 – Stage Check		1.5				1.5		
			1.0	As Req.	GL 27 – Instrument Rating End-of-Course Exam								
					FL 29 – End-of-Course Check		1.5				1.5		
6.0		1.5	2.0	As Req.	Stage Totals	(1.0)	11.0	8.0			11.0		
24.0	(5.0)	2.0	4.0	As Req.	Instrument Rating Course Totals	(10.0)	35.0	8.0			35.0		

NOTE: 1. Operators utilizing the PCATD option in the Instrument/Commercial or Instrument Rating Course may credit up to 5 hours of PCATD time toward ground training requirements.
2. Time listed for PCATD in flight training indicates use of the PCATD instead of the airplane for students utilizing the PCATD option.

LESSON TIME ALLOCATION

Ground Training						Flight Training							
						Dual					Solo		
Video, Class Discussion	PCATD	Pilot Briefings	Stage/Final Exams	Exam Debriefings		Day Local	Day Cross-Country	Night	Complex	Instrument	Day Local	Day Cross-Country	Night
					STAGE IV								
1.5					GL 28 – Airspace/Airports, Weather, (VFR) Charts								
1.5					GL 29 – Pilotage/Dead Reckoning (VFR)								
		As Req.			Briefing – Cross-Country Procedures (VFR)								
					FL 30 – Day Cross-Country (VFR)		3.0			As Req.			
2.0					GL 30 – Aviation Physiology								
					FL 31 – Night Local			1.0					
2.0					GL 31 – Aeronautical Decision Making								
					FL 32 – Night Cross-Country			4.0		As Req.			
2.0					GL 32 – Commercial FARs								
					FL 33 – Night Local Solo								1.5
					FL 34 – Night Local Solo								1.5
					FL 35 – Night Cross-Country Solo								3.0
			1.0	As Req.	GL 33 – Stage IV Exam								
					FL 36 – Cross-Country							5.0	
					FL 37 – Cross-Country							5.0	
					FL 38 – Cross-Country							5.0	
					FL 39 – Cross-Country							5.0	
					FL 40 – Cross-Country							5.0	
					FL 41 – Cross-Country							4.0	
					FL 42 – Cross-Country		3.0						
					FL 43 – Long Cross-Country							5.0	
					FL 44 – Stage IV Check		2.0						
9.0		As Req.	1.0	As Req.	Stage Totals		8.0	5.0				34.0	6.0

NOTE: 1. The individual times shown on the Lesson Time Allocation tables are for instructor/student guidance only; they are not mandatory for each flight, ground lesson, or stage of training. At the completion of this course, the student must meet the minimum requirements of FAR Part 141, for each category in order to graduate. Preflight and postflight briefings are as required.

2. Lessons 36 through 41 are designed for solo or dual flight as necessary to meet proficiency requirements for the end-of-course flight check and FAA practical test.

LESSON TIME ALLOCATION

Ground Training: Video, Class Discussion	Ground Training: PCATD	Ground Training: Pilot Briefings	Ground Training: Stage/Final Exams	Ground Training: Exam Debriefings		Flight Training: Dual: Day Local	Flight Training: Dual: Day Cross-Country	Flight Training: Dual: Night	Flight Training: Dual: Complex	Flight Training: Dual: Instrument	Flight Training: Solo: Day Local	Flight Training: Solo: Day Cross-Country	Flight Training: Solo: Night
					STAGE V								
					FL 45 – Basic Flight Maneuvers						1.0		
2.0					GL 34 – High Performance Powerplants								
2.0					GL 35 – Environmental and Ice Control Systems								
2.0					GL 36 – Retractable Landing Gear								
		As Req.			Briefing – Complex Aircraft Transition								
					FL 46 – Complex	1.0 (1.0)			1.0 (1.0)				
					FL 47 – Complex	1.5 (1.0)			1.5 (1.0)	As Req.			
2.0					GL 37 – Advanced Aerodynamics								
					FL 48 – Complex	1.5 (1.0)			1.5 (1.0)	As Req.			
2.0					GL 38 – Predicting Performance								
					FL 49 – Complex	2.0 (1.0)			2.0 (1.0)				
2.0					GL 39 – Controlling Weight and Balance								
					FL 50 – Complex	2.0 (1.0)			2.0 (1.0)				
		As Req.			Briefing – Commercial Flight Maneuvers								
2.0					GL 40 – Maximum Performance Takeoffs and Landings								
					FL 51 – Maximum Performance Takeoffs and Landings	1.5 (1.0)							
2.0					GL 41 – Steep Turns and Chandelles								
					FL 52 – Steep Turns and Chandelles	1.5 (1.0)							
2.0					GL 42 – Lazy 8s, Pylon 8s, Steep Spirals, and Accuracy Landings								
					FL 53 – Lazy 8s, Pylon 8s, Steep Spirals, and Accuracy Landings	1.5 (1.0)							
					FL 54 – Review Commercial Maneuvers						1.0		
					FL 55 – Review Commercial Maneuvers						1.0		
					FL 56 – Review Commercial Maneuvers						1.0		
					FL 57 – Review Commercial Maneuvers	1.5 (1.0)				As Req.			
2.0					GL 43 – Emergency Procedures								
					FL 58 – Review Commercial/Instrument	1.5 (1.0)				As Req.			
2.0					GL 44 – Commercial Decision Making								
					FL 59 – Commercial Maneuvers						1.0		
					FL 60 – Commercial Maneuvers						1.0		
					FL 61 – Commercial Maneuvers						1.0		
					FL 62 – Commercial Maneuvers						1.0		
					FL 63 – Commercial Maneuvers						1.0		
					FL 64 – Commercial Maneuvers	1.5 (1.0)							
					FL 65 – Commercial Maneuvers	1.0 (1.0)							
					FL 66 – Complex	1.0 (1.0)			1.0 (1.0)	As Req.			
			1.0	As Req.	GL 45 – Stage V Exam								
			2.0	As Req.	GL 46 – Commercial Pilot End-of-Course Exam								
					FL 67 – Stage V Check (Complex)	1.0 (1.0)			1.0 (1.0)	As Req.			
22.0		As Req.	3.0	As Req.	Stage Totals	20.0 (14.0)			10.0 (7.0)	As Req.	9.0		

NOTE: 1. In Stage V and VI, times in parentheses indicate lesson flight training times for students enrolled in the multi-engine option.

LESSON TIME ALLOCATION

Ground Training						Flight Training							
						Dual					Solo		
Video, Class Discussion	PCATD	Pilot Briefings	Stage/Final Exams	Exam Debriefings		Day Local	Day Cross-Country	Night	Complex	Instrument	Day Local	Day Cross-Country	Night
					FLIGHT STAGE VI								
					FL 68 – Instrument and Commercial Review	2.0 (1.0)				As Req.			
					FL 69 – Instrument/Commercial Maneuvers	2.0 (1.0)				As Req.			
					FL 70 – Practice Commercial						2.0		
					FL 71 – Practice Commercial						2.0		
					FL 72 – Commercial Review	2.0 (1.0)							
					FL 73 – Commercial Maneuvers						2.0		
					FL 74 – Commercial Maneuvers						2.0		
					FL 75 – Commercial Maneuvers						2.0		
					FL 76 – Commercial Review/Practice	2.0 (1.0)				As Req.			
					FL 77 – Commercial Review/Practice	2.0 (1.0)				As Req.			
					FL 78 – Complex Review	2.0 (1.0)			2.0 (1.0)				
					FL 79 – Solo Review						2.0		
					FL 80 – Solo Review						2.0		
					FL 81 – Solo Review						2.0		
					FL 82 – Complex Cross-Country		2.0 (1.0)		2.0 (1.0)	As Req.			
					FL 83 – Complex	1.0 (1.0)			1.0 (1.0)				
					FL 84 – Final Stage Review	2.0 (1.0)							
		As Req.			Briefing – Commercial Pilot Practical Test								
					FL 85 – Final Stage Review	2.0 (1.0)							
					FL 86 – Stage VI Check	1.5 (1.5)							
					FL 87 – End-of-Course Flight Check	1.5 (1.5)							
		As Req.			Stage Totals	20.0 (12.0)	2.0 (1.0)		5.0 (3.0)	As Req.	16.0		
31.0		As Req.	4.0	As Req.	Commercial Pilot Course Totals	40.0 (26.0)	10.0 (9.0)	5.0	15.0 (10.0)	As Req.	25.0	34.0	6.0

NOTE: 1. In Stages V and VI, times in parentheses indicate lesson flight training times for students enrolled in the multi-engine option.
2. Flight Training only is accomplished during this stage.

LESSON TIME ALLOCATION

Ground Training						Flight Training							
						Dual					Solo		
Video, Class Discussion	PCATD	Pilot Briefings	Stage/Final Exams	Exam Debriefings		Day Local	Day Cross-Country	Night	Complex	Instrument	Day Local	Day Cross-Country	Night
					GROUND STAGE VI AND FLIGHT STAGE VII								
2.0					GL 1 – The ME Rating, Human Factors, and Normal Ops.								
		.5			Briefing – Multi-Engine Operations and Systems								
					FL 1 – Introduction Multi-Engine Airplane and Maneuvers	1.0			1.0	.2			
1.5					GL 2 – Aircraft Systems, Wt. & Balance, & Performance								
		.5			Briefing – Performance Considerations								
					FL 2 – Basic Maneuvers – VR/IR	1.0			1.0	.2			
					FL 3 – Performance Maneuvers – VR/IR	1.0			1.0	.3			
1.5					GL 3 – ME/Engine-Out Aerodynamics & Maneuvers								
		.5			Briefing – Engine-Out Operations								
					FL 4 – Engine-Out Operations	1.0			1.0	.2			
1.5					GL 4 – Engine-Out Operations								
					FL 5 – Emergency Operations	1.0			1.0	.2			
					FL 6 – Review Engine-Out Operations	1.0			1.0	.2			
1.5					GL 5 – Instrument Flight and Decision Making								
		.5			Briefing – Multi-Engine Instrument Flight								
					FL 7 – Emergency Operations/Instrument Flight	1.0			1.0	.7			
					FL 8 – Multi-Engine Instrument (Day Cross-Country)		3.0		3.0	1.0			
					FL 9 – Multi-Engine Instrument (Night Cross-Country)			3.0	3.0	1.0			
			1.0	1.0	GL 6 – Stage Exam								
					FL 10 – Stage Check	1.0			1.0	.5			
			1.0	1.0	GL 7 – End-of-Course Exam								
					FL 11 – End-of-Course Check	1.0			1.0	.5			
8.0		2.0	2.0	2.0	Multi-Engine Stage Totals	9.0	3.0	3.0	15.0	5.0			

NOTE: 1. The dual instrument flight training time for Flight Lessons 2 through 11 is shown to indicate the recommended portion of these flights that should be devoted to instrument training.
2. This table covers Ground Stage VI and Flight Stage VII.

INSTRUMENT RATING STAGE I

STAGE OBJECTIVES

During this stage, the student will learn the principles of instrument flight, including the operation, use, and limitations of flight instruments and instrument navigation systems. The student will also learn how the air traffic control system functions and the use of instrument flight charts for IFR planning and flight. Emphasis will be placed on advanced human factors and physiological factors directly related to instrument flight. In addition, the student will become familiar with the FARs applicable to instrument flight operations.

STAGE COMPLETION STANDARDS

This stage is complete when the student has taken the Stage I Exam with a minimum passing score of 80%, and the instructor has reviewed each incorrect response to ensure complete understanding before the student progresses to Stage II.

STAGE I GROUND LESSON 1

LESSON REFERENCES:

INSTRUMENT/COMMERCIAL

Chapter 1, Building Professional Experience

RECOMMENDED SEQUENCE:

NOTE: *Students should read Chapter 1, Sections A and B, prior to Ground Lesson 1.*

1. Lesson Introduction
2. Class Discussion

LESSON OBJECTIVES:

- Review knowledge of private pilot privileges.
- Become familiar with advanced pilot training and opportunities.
- Gain an understanding of the advanced human factors concepts related to aviation.

ACADEMIC CONTENT:

COURSE OVERVIEW

- ❑ Course Elements
- ❑ Course Materials
- ❑ Exams and Tests
- ❑ Policies and Procedures
- ❑ Personal Computer-Based Aviation Training Device (PCATD) Utilization
- ❑ Student/Instructor Expectations
- ❑ Review Private Pilot Privileges and Limitations

SECTION A — INSTRUMENT/COMMERCIAL TRAINING AND OPPORTUNITIES

- ❑ Instrument Flight
- ❑ Instrument/Commercial Training
- ❑ Commercial Pilot Privileges
- ❑ Additional Certificates and Ratings

SECTION B — ADVANCED HUMAN FACTORS CONCEPTS

- ❑ Aeronautical Decision Making
- ❑ Crew Resource Management
- ❑ Single-Pilot Resource Management
- ❑ The Decision-Making Process
- ❑ Pilot-in-Command Responsibility
- ❑ Communication
- ❑ Workload Management
- ❑ Situational Awareness

AVIATION PHYSIOLOGY

- ❑ Spatial Disorientation
- ❑ Vestibular Disorientation
- ❑ Motion Sickness
- ❑ Hypoxia
- ❑ Prevention of Hypoxia
- ❑ Decompression Sickness
- ❑ Hyperventilation
- ❑ Stress
- ❑ Fatigue

- ❑ Alcohol and Drugs
- ❑ Fitness for Flight

COMPLETION STANDARDS:

- The student will indicate, through oral quizzing, familiarity with instrument/commercial training, opportunities in aviation, human factors, and understanding of private pilot privileges. In addition, the instructor will make sure the student has a basic understanding of policies and procedures applicable to the school's pilot training program.

STUDY ASSIGNMENT:

INSTRUMENT/COMMERCIAL

Chapter 2, Section A — Flight Instrument Systems

STAGE I
GROUND LESSON 2

LESSON REFERENCES:

INSTRUMENT/COMMERCIAL

Chapter 2, Section A — Flight Instrument Systems

GFD I/C VIDEO

Part 1, Chapter 2, Section A

RECOMMENDED SEQUENCE:

1. Lesson Introduction and Video Presentation
2. Class Discussion

LESSON OBJECTIVES:

- Gain a working knowledge of the function and use of the flight instrument components and systems.
- Become familiar with the limitations and common errors of the flight instrument systems and components.

ACADEMIC CONTENT:

SECTION A — FLIGHT INSTRUMENT SYSTEMS

- ❑ FAA Instrument Requirements

GYROSCOPIC FLIGHT INSTRUMENTS

- ❑ System Operation
- ❑ System Errors
- ❑ Instrument Check

MAGNETIC COMPASS

- ❑ System Operation
- ❑ System Errors
- ❑ Instrument Check

PITOT-STATIC INSTRUMENTS

- ❑ System Operation
- ❑ System Errors
- ❑ Instrument Check
- ❑ V-Speeds and Color Codes

INTEGRATED DISPLAYS

- ❑ Primary Flight Display
- ❑ Multifunction Display
- ❑ Malfunctions and Failures

COMPLETION STANDARDS:

- Demonstrate understanding of IFR instrument requirements as well as instrument flight systems, instrument operations, and instrument errors during oral quizzing by instructor at completion of lesson.
- Student completes Chapter 2 questions for Section A with a minimum passing score of 80%, and the instructor reviews incorrect responses to ensure complete understanding before the student progresses to Ground Lesson 3.

STUDY ASSIGNMENT:

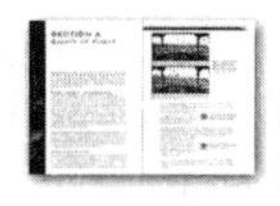

INSTRUMENT/COMMERCIAL

Chapter 2, Section B — Attitude Instrument Flying

STAGE I
GROUND LESSON 3

LESSON REFERENCES:

INSTRUMENT/COMMERCIAL
Chapter 2, Section B — Attitude Instrument Flying

GFD I/C VIDEO
Part 1, Chapter 2, Section B

PCATD

RECOMMENDED SEQUENCE:

1. Lesson Introduction and Video Presentation
2. Class Discussion
3. PCATD

LESSON OBJECTIVES:

- Review the basic principles of attitude instrument flying, including the fundamental procedures related to instrument cross-check, instrument interpretation, and aircraft control.
- Gain a working knowledge of the instrument cockpit check.
- Become familiar with instrument system failures and partial panel flight procedures.

ACADEMIC CONTENT:

SECTION B — ATTITUDE INSTRUMENT FLYING

FUNDAMENTAL SKILLS

❑ Instrument Cross-Check
❑ Instrument Interpretation
❑ Aircraft Control
❑ Control and Performance Concept
❑ Primary/Support Concept

BASIC FLIGHT MANEUVERS

❑ Straight-and-Level Flight
❑ Standard-Rate Turns
❑ Steep Turns
❑ Constant Airspeed Climbs
❑ Constant Rate Climbs
❑ Constant Airspeed Descents
❑ Constant Rate Descents
❑ Leveloff From Climbs and Descents
❑ Climbing and Descending Turns
❑ Stalls

COPING WITH INSTRUMENT FAILURE

❑ Identifying an Instrument Failure
❑ Attitude Indicator Failure
❑ Heading Indicator Failure
❑ Partial Panel Flying
❑ Magnetic Compass Turns
❑ Timed Turns
❑ Pitot-Static Instrument Failures

UNUSUAL ATTITUDE RECOVERY

❑ Nose-High Attitude
❑ Nose-Low Attitude
❑ Partial Panel Unusual Attitude Recovery

INTRODUCTION TO THE PCATD (OPTION)

❑ Orientation and Flight Familiarization
❑ Overview of Physical and Virtual Controls
❑ Aircraft Systems Related to IFR Operations
❑ Instrument Cockpit Check
❑ Full Panel Instrument Maneuvers
❑ Partial Panel Instrument Considerations

COMPLETION STANDARDS:

- Demonstrate understanding of basic attitude instrument flight during oral quizzing by instructor at completion of lesson.
- Exhibit knowledge of partial panel instrument flight procedures.
- Student completes Chapter 2 questions for Section B with a minimum passing score of 80%, and the instructor reviews incorrect responses to ensure complete student understanding before the student progresses to Ground Lesson 4.

STUDY ASSIGNMENT:

INSTRUMENT/COMMERCIAL
Chapter 2, Section C — Instrument Navigation

STAGE I

GROUND LESSON 4

LESSON REFERENCES:

INSTRUMENT/COMMERCIAL

Chapter 2, Section C — Instrument Navigation

GFD I/C VIDEO
Part 1, Chapter 2, Section C

PCATD

RECOMMENDED SEQUENCE:

1. Lesson Introduction and Video Presentation
2. Class Discussion
3. PCATD

LESSON OBJECTIVES:

- Learn the function, use, and limitations of VOR, DME, and ADF radio equipment navigation aids (navaids).
- Become familiar with other types of instrument navigation including RNAV and VNAV.

ACADEMIC CONTENT:

SECTION C — INSTRUMENT NAVIGATION

VOR NAVIGATION

❑ Horizontal Situation Indicator
❑ Intercepting a Radial
❑ Tracking
❑ Determining Your Progress
❑ Time and Distance to a Station
❑ Station Passage
❑ VOR Limitations
❑ Distance Measuring Equipment
❑ DME Arcs

ADF NAVIGATION

❑ Automatic Direction Finder
❑ Radio Magnetic Indicator
❑ Intercepting a Bearing
❑ Tracking
❑ Time and Distance to a Station
❑ Station Passage

OPERATIONAL CONSIDERATIONS

❑ Ground Facilities
❑ VOR Checks
❑ Identification

AREA NAVIGATION (RNAV)

❑ VORTAC-Based Area Navigation
❑ Flight Management Systems (FMS)
❑ Inertial Navigation System (INS)
❑ Global Positioning System (GPS)
❑ GNSS Landing System(GLS)
❑ Global Navigation Satellite System (GNSS)
❑ Long Range Navigation (LORAN)

PCATD (OPTION)

❑ VOR Orientation
❑ Intercepting and Tracking a VOR Radial
❑ VOR Time, Speed and Distance Computations
❑ Intercepting and Tracking DME Arcs
❑ NDB Orientation
❑ NDB Homing
❑ Intercepting and Tracking NDB Bearings
❑ RNAV Orientation (If Available)
❑ HSI and RMI Orientation (If Available)
❑ Electronic Flight Instrument Display (If Available)
❑ Analysis of Ground Tracks

COMPLETION STANDARDS:

- Demonstrate understanding of the use and limitations of navigation systems during oral quizzing by instructor at completion of lesson.
- Student completes Chapter 2 questions for Section C with a minimum passing score of 80%, and the instructor will review each incorrect response to ensure complete understanding before the student progresses to Ground Lesson 5.

STUDY ASSIGNMENT:

FAR/AIM
Instrument FARs

STAGE I
GROUND LESSON 5

LESSON REFERENCES:

FAR/AIM
Instrument FARs

RECOMMENDED SEQUENCE:

1. Lesson Introduction
2. Class Discussion

LESSON OBJECTIVES:

- Become familiar with the Federal Aviation Regulations related to instrument flight.
- Understand the information from NTSB Part 830.

ACADEMIC CONTENT:

- ❑ FAR Part 1
- ❑ FAR Part 61
- ☒ FAR Part 91
- ❑ NTSB Part 830

COMPLETION STANDARDS:

- Student demonstrates understanding of the resources and regulations related to instrument flight during oral quizzing by instructor.
- The student will complete the Instrument Rating (Airplane) Exercises in the FAR/AIM with a minimum passing score of 80%, and the instructor will review each incorrect response to ensure complete understanding before the student progresses to Ground Lesson 6.

STUDY ASSIGNMENT:

INSTRUMENT/COMMERCIAL

Chapter 3, Section A — Airports, Airspace, and Flight Information

---

STAGE I
GROUND LESSON 6

LESSON REFERENCES:

INSTRUMENT/COMMERCIAL

Chapter 3, Section A — Airports, Airspace, and Flight Information

GFD I/C VIDEO
Part 1, Chapter 3, Section A

RECOMMENDED SEQUENCE:

1. Lesson Introduction and Video Presentation
2. Class Discussion

LESSON OBJECTIVES:

- Study and become familiar with the airport environment, including collision avoidance, and runway incursion avoidance.
- Gain specific knowledge of the National Airspace System.
- Gain a basic understanding of the sources of flight information, particularly the *Aeronautical Information Manual* and FAA Advisory Circulars dealing with IFR flight.

ACADEMIC CONTENT:

SECTION A — AIRPORTS, AIRSPACE, AND FLIGHT INFORMATION

AIRPORT ENVIRONMENT

- ❑ Runway Markings
- ❑ Taxiway Markings
- ❑ Airport Signs
- ❑ Runway Incursion Avoidance
- ❑ Land and Hold Short Operations (LAHSO)
- ❑ Approach Light System
- ❑ Visual Glide Slope Indicators
- ❑ Runway Lighting
- ❑ Airport Beacons and Obstruction Lights

AIRSPACE

- ❑ Controlled Airspace
- ❑ Class A, B, C, D, and E Airspace
- ❑ Special VFR
- ❑ Class G Airspace (Uncontrolled)

- ❑ Aircraft Speed Limits
- ❑ Special Use Airspace
- ❑ Other Airspace Areas
- ❑ ADIZ

FLIGHT INFORMATION

- ❑ *Aeronautical Information Manual*
- ❑ *Airport/Facility Directory*
- ❑ Notices to Airmen (NOTAMs)
- ❑ Flight Data Center
- ❑ *International Flight Information Manual*
- ❑ Advisory Circulars
- ❑ Jeppesen Information Services
- ❑ Electronic Flight Publications
- ❑ Government Printing Office

COMPLETION STANDARDS:

- Demonstrate understanding of the airport environment and lighting, as well as airspace usage and sources of flight information during oral quizzing by instructor at completion of lesson.
- Student completes Chapter 3 questions for Section A with a minimum passing score of 80%, and the instructor reviews incorrect responses to ensure complete understanding before the student progresses to Ground Lesson 7.

STUDY ASSIGNMENT:

INSTRUMENT/COMMERCIAL

Chapter 3, Section B — Air Traffic Control System

STAGE I GROUND LESSON 7

LESSON REFERENCES:

INSTRUMENT/COMMERCIAL

Chapter 3, Section B —Air Traffic Control System

GFD I/C VIDEO

Part 1, Chapter 3, Section B

RECOMMENDED SEQUENCE:

1. Lesson Introduction and Video Presentation
2. Class Discussion

LESSON OBJECTIVES:

- Learn the types of services provided by the air traffic control system.
- Become familiar with the various enroute and terminal facilities and their use for flight under IFR.

ACADEMIC CONTENT:

SECTION B — AIR TRAFFIC CONTROL SYSTEM

- ❑ Air Route Traffic Control Center
- ❑ ARTCC Traffic Separation
- ❑ Processing the IFR Flight Plan
- ❑ Weather Information
- ❑ Safety Alerts
- ❑ Emergency Assistance
- ❑ Terminal Facilities
- ❑ ATIS
- ❑ Clearance Delivery
- ❑ Control Tower
- ❑ Approach and Departure Control
- ❑ Radar Service for VFR Aircraft
- ❑ Flight Service Stations

COMPLETION STANDARDS:

- Demonstrate understanding of enroute and terminal ATC services during oral quizzing by instructor at completion of lesson.
- Student completes Chapter 3 questions for Section B with a minimum passing score of 80%, and the instructor reviews incorrect responses to ensure complete student understanding before the student progresses to Ground Lesson 8.

STUDY ASSIGNMENT:

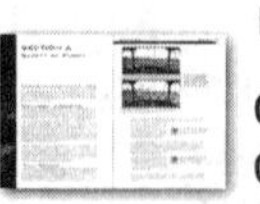

INSTRUMENT/COMMERCIAL

Chapter 3, Section C —ATC Clearances

STAGE I
GROUND LESSON 8

LESSON REFERENCES:

INSTRUMENT/COMMERCIAL
Chapter 3, Section C — ATC Clearances

GFD I/C VIDEO
Part 1, Chapter 3, Section C

RECOMMENDED SEQUENCE:

1. Lesson Introduction and Video Presentation
2. Class Discussion

LESSON OBJECTIVES:

- Become familiar with ATC clearance procedures.
- Learn and gain experience using clearance shorthand.

ACADEMIC CONTENT:

SECTION C — ATC CLEARANCES

❑ Pilot Responsibilities
❑ IFR Flight Plan and ATC Clearance
❑ Elements of an IFR Clearance
❑ Abbreviated IFR Departure Clearance
❑ VFR on Top
❑ Approach Clearances
❑ VFR Restrictions to an IFR Clearance
❑ Composite Flight Plan
❑ Tower Enroute Control Clearance
❑ Departure Restrictions
❑ Clearance Readback
❑ Clearance Shorthand

COMPLETION STANDARDS:

- Demonstrate understanding of pilot responsibilities and clearance procedures during oral quizzing by instructor at completion of lesson.
- Student completes Chapter 3 questions for Section C with a minimum passing score of 80%, and the instructor reviews incorrect responses to ensure complete student understanding before the student progresses to the Stage I Exam in Ground Lesson 9.

STUDY ASSIGNMENT:

INSTRUMENT/COMMERCIAL
Review Chapters 1, 2, and 3 in preparation for the Stage I Exam.

STAGE I
GROUND LESSON 9

STAGE I EXAM

LESSON REFERENCES:

INSTRUMENT/COMMERCIAL
Chapters 1, 2, and 3

FAR/AIM
Instrument FARs

RECOMMENDED SEQUENCE:

1. Lesson Introduction
2. Testing
3. Critique

LESSON OBJECTIVES:

- Administer the stage exam covering the first three chapters of the *Instrument/Commercial* textbook, the applicable FARs, and NTSB Part 830 rules.

ACADEMIC CONTENT:

STAGE I EXAM

❑ Advanced Human Factors Concepts
❑ Flight Instrument Systems
❑ Attitude Instrument Flying
❑ Instrument Navigation
❑ Airports, Airspace, and Flight Information
❑ Air Traffic Control System

- ❏ FAR/AIM and NTSB Part 830
- ❏ Air Traffic Control Clearances

COMPLETION STANDARDS:

- The lesson and stage are complete when the student has completed the Stage I Exam with a minimum passing score of 80%, and the instructor has reviewed each incorrect response to ensure complete understanding before the student progresses to Stage II.

STUDY ASSIGNMENT:

INSTRUMENT/COMMERCIAL

Chapter 4, Section A — Departure Charts and Departure Procedures

STAGE II

STAGE OBJECTIVES

During this stage, the student will learn the procedures used to execute the various IFR approaches as well as the procedures for IFR departure, enroute, and arrival operations.

STAGE COMPLETION STANDARDS

This stage is complete when the student has taken the Stage II Exam with a minimum passing score of 80%, and the instructor has reviewed each incorrect response to ensure complete understanding before the student progresses to Stage III.

STAGE II GROUND LESSON 10

LESSON REFERENCES:

INSTRUMENT/COMMERCIAL

Chapter 4, Departure

GFD I/C VIDEO

Part II, Chapter 4, Sections A and B

RECOMMENDED SEQUENCE:

1. Lesson Introduction and Video Presentation
2. Class Discussion

LESSON OBJECTIVES:

- Learn the format and symbology used to present information on departure charts.
- Gain a working knowledge of departure procedures.

ACADEMIC CONTENT:

SECTION A — DEPARTURE CHARTS

❑ Obtaining Charts
❑ Departure Standards
❑ Instrument Departure Procedures (DPs)
❑ Obstacle Departure Procedures (ODPs)
❑ Standard Instrument Departures (SIDs)
❑ Pilot Nav DP
❑ Vector DP
❑ Chart Format and Symbology

SECTION B — DEPARTURE PROCEDURES

❑ Takeoff Minimums
❑ Departure Options
❑ Graphic Departure Procedures
❑ Textual Departure Procedures
❑ Radar Departures
❑ VFR Departures
❑ Selecting a Departure Method

COMPLETION STANDARDS:

- Demonstrate understanding of instrument departure procedures and related considerations during oral quizzing by instructor at completion of lesson.
- Student completes Chapter 4 questions for Sections A and B with a minimum passing score of 80%, and the instructor reviews incorrect responses to ensure complete student understanding before the student progresses to Ground Lesson 11.

STUDY ASSIGNMENT:

INSTRUMENT/COMMERCIAL

Chapter 5, Section A — Enroute and Area Charts, and Section B — Enroute Procedures

STAGE II
GROUND LESSON 11

LESSON REFERENCES:

INSTRUMENT/COMMERCIAL

Chapter 5, Section A — Enroute and Area Charts, and Section B — Enroute Procedures

GFD I/C VIDEO

Part II, Segment 1, Chapter 5, Sections A and B

RECOMMENDED SEQUENCE:

1. Lesson Introduction and Video Presentation
2. Class Discussion

LESSON OBJECTIVES:

- Gain a working knowledge of enroute and area charts.
- Learn the symbology used to present information and the applicable procedures for IFR enroute operations.

ACADEMIC CONTENT:

SECTION A — ENROUTE AND AREA CHARTS

- ❑ Enroute Charts
- ❑ Front Panel
- ❑ Navigation Aids
- ❑ Victor Airways
- ❑ Communication
- ❑ Airports
- ❑ Airspace
- ❑ Area Charts

SECTION B — ENROUTE PROCEDURES

- ❑ Enroute Radar Procedures
- ❑ Communication
- ❑ Reporting Procedures
- ❑ Enroute Navigation Using GPS
- ❑ Air Traffic Service Routes
- ❑ Enroute RNP
- ❑ Special Use Airspace
- ❑ Temporary Flight Restrictions
- ❑ IFR Cruising and Minimum Altitudes
- ❑ Descending from the Enroute Segment
- ❑ Reduced Vertical Separation Minimum

COMPLETION STANDARDS:

- Demonstrate understanding of enroute charts as well as enroute navigation and communication procedures during oral quizzing by instructor at completion of lesson.
- Student completes Chapter 5 questions for Sections A and B with a minimum passing score of 80%, and the instructor reviews incorrect responses to ensure complete understanding before the student progresses to Ground Lesson 12.

STUDY ASSIGNMENT:

INSTRUMENT/COMMERCIAL

Chapter 5, Section C — Holding Procedures

STAGE II
GROUND LESSON 12

LESSON REFERENCES:

INSTRUMENT/COMMERCIAL

Chapter 5, Section C — Holding Procedures

GFD I/C VIDEO

Part II, Segment 1, Chapter 5, Section C

PCATD

RECOMMENDED SEQUENCE:

1. Lesson Introduction and Video Presentation
2. Class Discussion
3. PCATD

LESSON OBJECTIVES:

- Gain a working knowledge of holding patterns including entry, timing, and communication.

ACADEMIC CONTENT:

SECTION C — HOLDING PROCEDURES

- ❑ Standard and Nonstandard Pattern
- ❑ Outbound and Inbound Timing

- ❑ Crosswind Correction
- ❑ Maximum Holding Speed
- ❑ Direct Entry
- ❑ Teardrop Entry
- ❑ Parallel Entry
- ❑ Visualizing Entry Procedures
- ❑ ATC Holding Instructions

PCATD (OPTION)

- ❑ ATC Holding Instructions
- ❑ Holding Entry
- ❑ VOR Holding
- ❑ NDB Holding
- ❑ Standard and Nonstandard Holding
- ❑ Wind Correction and Ground Track

COMPLETION STANDARDS:

- Demonstrate understanding of holding entry and procedures during oral quizzing by instructor at completion of lesson.
- Student completes Chapter 5 questions for Section C with a minimum passing score of 80%, and the instructor reviews incorrect responses to ensure complete understanding before the student progresses to Ground Lesson 13.

STUDY ASSIGNMENT:

INSTRUMENT/COMMERCIAL

Chapter 6, Arrival

STAGE II GROUND LESSON 13

LESSON REFERENCES:

INSTRUMENT/COMMERCIAL

Chapter 6, Arrival

GFD I/C VIDEO

Part II, Segment 1, Chapter 6, Sections A and B

RECOMMENDED SEQUENCE:

1. Lesson Introduction and Video Presentation
2. Class Discussion

LESSON OBJECTIVES:

- Gain a working knowledge of arrival charts.
- Gain a working knowledge of arrival procedures and methods.

ACADEMIC CONTENT:

SECTION A — ARRIVAL CHARTS

- ❑ Standard Terminal Arrival Route
- ❑ Interpreting the STAR
- ❑ Vertical Navigation Planning

SECTION B — ARRIVAL PROCEDURES

- ❑ Preparing for the Arrival
- ❑ Reviewing the Approach
- ❑ Altitude
- ❑ Airspeed

COMPLETION STANDARDS:

- Demonstrate understanding of arrival charts and procedures during oral quizzing by instructor at completion of lesson.
- Student completes Chapter 6 questions for Sections A, and B with a minimum passing score of 80%, and the instructor reviews incorrect responses to ensure complete understanding before the student progresses to Ground Lesson 14.

STUDY ASSIGNMENT:

INSTRUMENT/COMMERCIAL

Chapter 7, Section A — Approach Charts

STAGE II
GROUND LESSON 14

LESSON REFERENCES:

INSTRUMENT/COMMERCIAL
Chapter 7, Section A — Approach Charts

GFD I/C VIDEO
Part II, Segment II, Chapter 7, Section A

RECOMMENDED SEQUENCE:

1. Lesson Introduction and Video Presentation
2. Class Discussion

LESSON OBJECTIVES:

- The student will begin to learn how to interpret and use information published on instrument approach charts.

ACADEMIC CONTENT:

SECTION A — APPROACH CHARTS

APPROACH SEGMENTS

❑ Initial Approach Segment
❑ Intermediate Approach Segment
❑ Final Approach Segment
❑ Missed Approach Segment

CHART LAYOUT

❑ Heading Section
❑ Briefing Information
❑ Minimum Safe Altitude
❑ Plan View
❑ Feeder Routes
❑ Profile View
❑ Step Down Fix and VDP
❑ Missed Approach Icons
❑ Conversion Table
❑ Landing Minimums
❑ Aircraft Approach Categories
❑ Minimum Descent Requirements
❑ Visibility Requirements
❑ Inoperative Components

AIRPORT CHART

❑ Heading and Communications Sections
❑ Plan View and Additional Runway Information
❑ Takeoff and Alternate Minimums

APPROACH CHART FORMAT CHANGES

COMPLETION STANDARDS:

- Demonstrate understanding of instrument approach charts during oral quizzing by instructor at completion of lesson.
- Student completes Chapter 7 questions for Section A with a minimum passing score of 80%, and the instructor reviews incorrect responses to ensure complete understanding before the student progresses to Ground Lesson 15.

STUDY ASSIGNMENT:

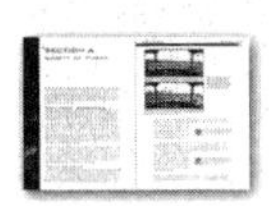

INSTRUMENT/COMMERCIAL
Chapter 7, Section B — Approach Procedures

STAGE II
GROUND LESSON 15

LESSON REFERENCES:

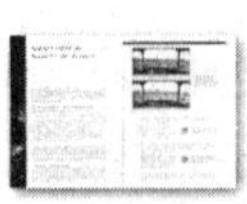

INSTRUMENT/COMMERCIAL
Chapter 7, Section B — Approach Procedures

GFD I/C VIDEO
Part II, Segment II, Chapter 7, Section B

RECOMMENDED SEQUENCE:

1. Lesson Introduction and Video Presentation
2. Class Discussion

LESSON OBJECTIVES:

- Learn the procedures used to transition from the enroute segment to the approach segment.
- Increase understanding and knowledge of approach procedures.

ACADEMIC CONTENT:

SECTION B — APPROACH PROCEDURES

- ❏ Preparing for the Approach
- ❏ Approach Chart Review
- ❏ Approach Clearance
- ❏ Executing the Approach
- ❏ Straight-In Approaches
- ❏ Use of ATC Radar for Approaches
- ❏ Approaches Which Require a Course Reversal
- ❏ Timed Approaches From a Holding Fix
- ❏ Final Approach
- ❏ Circling Approaches
- ❏ Sidestep Maneuver
- ❏ Missed Approach Procedures
- ❏ Visual and Contact Approaches

COMPLETION STANDARDS:

- Demonstrate understanding of approach operations and procedures during oral quizzing by instructor at completion of lesson.
- Student completes Chapter 7 questions for Section B with a minimum passing score of 80%, and the instructor reviews incorrect responses to ensure complete understanding before the student progresses to Ground Lesson 16.

STUDY ASSIGNMENT:

INSTRUMENT/COMMERCIAL

Chapter 8, Section A — VOR and NDB Approaches

STAGE II GROUND LESSON 16

LESSON REFERENCES:

INSTRUMENT/COMMERCIAL

Chapter 8, Section A — VOR and NDB Approaches

GFD I/C VIDEO

Part II, Segment II, Chapter 8, Section A

PCATD

RECOMMENDED SEQUENCE:

1. Lesson Introduction and Video Presentation
2. Class Discussion
3. PCATD

LESSON OBJECTIVES:

- Learn procedures and methods necessary to perform VOR and NDB approaches.

ACADEMIC CONTENT:

SECTION A — VOR AND NDB APPROACHES

- ❏ VOR Approach Procedure
- ❏ Off-Airport Facility
- ❏ On-Airport Facility
- ❏ VOR/DME Approach Procedures
- ❏ NDB Approach Procedure
- ❏ Radar Vectors to the Approach

PCATD (OPTION)

- ❏ VOR Approach Procedure
- ❏ VOR Missed Approach Procedure
- ❏ NDB Approach Procedure
- ❏ NDB Missed Approach Procedure

COMPLETION STANDARDS:

- Demonstrate understanding of VOR and NDB approach procedures during oral quizzing by instructor at completion of lesson.
- Student completes Chapter 8 questions for Section A with a minimum passing score of 80%, and the instructor reviews incorrect responses to ensure complete understanding before the student progresses to Ground Lesson 17.

STUDY ASSIGNMENT:

INSTRUMENT/COMMERCIAL

Chapter 8, Section B — ILS Approaches

STAGE II
GROUND LESSON 17

LESSON REFERENCES:

INSTRUMENT/COMMERCIAL
Chapter 8, Section B — ILS Approaches

GFD I/C VIDEO
Part II, Segment II, Chapter 8, Section B

PCATD

RECOMMENDED SEQUENCE:

1. Lesson Introduction and Video Presentation
2. Class Discussion
3. PCATD

LESSON OBJECTIVES:

- Gain knowledge of ILS components and approach procedures.

SECTION B — ILS APPROACHES

- ❏ ILS Categories and Minimums
- ❏ ILS Components
- ❏ Inoperative Components
- ❏ Flying the ILS
- ❏ Straight-In (NoPT) ILS Approach
- ❏ ILS Approach With a Course Reversal
- ❏ ILS/DME Approach
- ❏ Radar Vectors to ILS Final
- ❏ ILS Approaches to Parallel Runways
- ❏ Simultaneous Converging Instrument Approach
- ❏ Localizer Approach
- ❏ Localizer Back Course Approach
- ❏ LDA, SDF, and MLS Approaches

PCATD (OPTION)

- ❏ Localizer
- ❏ Glideslope
- ❏ ILS Marker Beacons
- ❏ Compass Locators
- ❏ ILS Visual Aids
- ❏ ILS Categories
- ❏ Flying the ILS Approach
- ❏ Nonradar ILS Procedures
- ❏ Transition Via DME Arc
- ❏ NDB Transition
- ❏ ILS Procedures with Radar
- ❏ ILS Procedures with DME
- ❏ Back Course Approaches

COMPLETION STANDARDS:

- Demonstrate understanding of the various methods of conducting an ILS approach during oral quizzing by instructor at completion of lesson.
- Student completes Chapter 8 questions for Section B with a minimum passing score of 80%, and the instructor reviews incorrect responses to ensure complete understanding before the student progresses to Ground Lesson 18.

STUDY ASSIGNMENT:

INSTRUMENT/COMMERCIAL
Chapter 8, Section C — RNAV Approaches

STAGE II
GROUND LESSON 18

LESSON REFERENCES:

INSTRUMENT/COMMERCIAL

Chapter 8, Section C — RNAV Approaches

RECOMMENDED SEQUENCE:

1. Lesson Introduction
2. Class Discussion

LESSON OBJECTIVES:

- Become familiar with RNAV instrument approach systems and procedures.

ACADEMIC CONTENT:

SECTION C — RNAV APPROACHES

- ❑ Approach Design
- ❑ Terminal Arrival Area
- ❑ Waypoints
- ❑ Required Navigation Performance
- ❑ GPS Approaches
- ❑ Lateral Navigation/Vertical Navigation
- ❑ VNAV Descent Profile
- ❑ Approach with Vertical Guidance (APV)
- ❑ Precision Approaches
- ❑ GPS Equipment Requirements
- ❑ Receiver Autonomous Integrity Monitoring
- ❑ The Navigation Database
- ❑ GPS Navigation Considerations
- ❑ GPS Overlay Approach
- ❑ GPS Stand-Alone/RNAV (GPS) Approach
- ❑ Radar Vectors to a GPS Approach

VOR/DME RNAV

- ❑ Operating Principles
- ❑ VOR DME RNAV Approaches

COMPLETION STANDARDS:

- Demonstrate understanding of RNAV approach procedures and limitations during oral quizzing by instructor at completion of lesson.
- Student completes Chapter 8 questions for Section C with a minimum passing score of 80% and the instructor reviews incorrect responses to ensure complete understanding before the student progresses to the Stage II Exam in Lesson 19.

STUDY ASSIGNMENT:

INSTRUMENT/COMMERCIAL

Review Chapters 4 – 8 in preparation for the Stage II Exam.

STAGE II GROUND LESSON 19

STAGE II EXAM

LESSON REFERENCES:

INSTRUMENT/COMMERCIAL

Chapters 4 – 8

RECOMMENDED SEQUENCE:

1. Lesson Introduction
2. Testing
3. Critique

LESSON OBJECTIVES:

- Administer the stage exam to evaluate the student's comprehension of enroute and terminal chart information, as well as the applicable procedures covered in chapters 4, 5, 6, 7, and 8.

ACADEMIC CONTENT:

STAGE II EXAM

❑ Departure Charts and Procedures
❑ Enroute Charts and Procedures
❑ Holding Procedures
❑ Arrival Charts and Procedures
❑ Approach Charts and Procedures
❑ VOR and NDB Instrument Approaches
❑ ILS Approaches
❑ RNAV Approaches

COMPLETION STANDARDS:

- The lesson and stage are complete when the student has completed the Stage II Exam with a minimum passing score of 80%, and the instructor has reviewed each incorrect response to ensure complete understanding before the student progresses to Stage III.

STUDY ASSIGNMENT:

INSTRUMENT/COMMERCIAL

Chapter 9, Section A — Weather Factors and Section B — Weather Hazards

STAGE III

STAGE OBJECTIVES

During this stage, the student will learn to analyze weather information, conditions, and trends while on the ground and in flight. In addition, the student will learn IFR flight planning and emergency procedures and develop a greater understanding of the decision-making process.

STAGE COMPLETION STANDARDS

This stage is complete when the student has successfully taken the Stage III Exam and the Instrument Rating End-of-Course Exam with minimum passing scores of 80%, and the instructor has reviewed each incorrect response to ensure complete student understanding.

STAGE III GROUND LESSON 20

LESSON REFERENCES:

INSTRUMENT/COMMERCIAL Chapter 9, Section A — Weather Factors and Section B — Weather Hazards

GFD I/C VIDEO
Part III, Chapter 9, Sections A and B

RECOMMENDED SEQUENCE:

1. Lesson Introduction and Video Presentation
2. Class Discussion

LESSON OBJECTIVES:

- Become familiar with the factors affecting weather patterns and hazards related to flight operations.

ACADEMIC CONTENT:

SECTION A — WEATHER FACTORS

- ❑ The Atmosphere
- ❑ Atmospheric Circulation
- ❑ Pressure and Wind Patterns
- ❑ Moisture, Precipitation, and Stability
- ❑ Types of Clouds
- ❑ Airmass
- ❑ Fronts
- ❑ High Altitude Weather

SECTION B — WEATHER HAZARDS

- ❑ Recognition of Critical Weather Situations
- ❑ Thunderstorms
- ❑ Thunderstorm Avoidance
- ❑ Low Level Turbulence
- ❑ Turbulence
- ❑ Wake Turbulence
- ❑ Clear Air Turbulence
- ❑ Mountain Wave Turbulence
- ❑ Reporting Turbulence
- ❑ Wind Shear
- ❑ Low Visibility
- ❑ Volcanic Ash
- ❑ Icing
- ❑ Hydroplaning
- ❑ Cold Weather Operations

COMPLETION STANDARDS:

- Demonstrate understanding of weather factors and weather hazards during oral quizzing by instructor at completion of lesson.
- Student completes Chapter 9 questions for Sections A and B with a minimum passing score of 80%, and the instructor reviews incorrect responses to ensure complete understanding before the student progresses to Ground Lesson 21.

STUDY ASSIGNMENT:

INSTRUMENT/COMMERCIAL
Chapter 9, Section C — Printed Reports and Forecasts

STAGE III
GROUND LESSON 21

LESSON REFERENCES:

INSTRUMENT/COMMERCIAL

Chapter 9, Section C — Printed Reports and Forecasts

GFD I/C VIDEO
Part III, Chapter 9, Section C

RECOMMENDED SEQUENCE:

1. Lesson Introduction and Video Presentation
2. Class Discussion

LESSON OBJECTIVES:

- Learn to retrieve and interpret printed weather reports and forecasts.

ACADEMIC CONTENT:

SECTION C — PRINTED REPORTS AND FORECASTS

❑ Aviation Routine Weather Report (METAR)
❑ Radar Weather Reports
❑ Pilot Weather Reports
❑ Terminal Aerodrome Forecast
❑ Aviation Area Forecast
❑ Winds and Temperatures Aloft Forecast
❑ Severe Weather Reports and Forecasts

COMPLETION STANDARDS:

- Demonstrate understanding of information contained in printed reports and forecasts during oral quizzing by instructor at completion of lesson.
- Student completes Chapter 9 questions for Section C with a minimum passing score of 80%, and the instructor reviews incorrect responses to ensure complete understanding before the student progresses to Ground Lesson 22.

STUDY ASSIGNMENT:

INSTRUMENT/COMMERCIAL

Chapter 9, Section D — Graphic Weather Products

STAGE III
GROUND LESSON 22

LESSON REFERENCES:

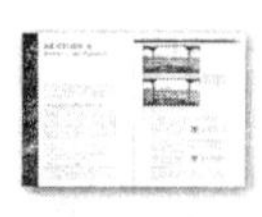

INSTRUMENT/COMMERCIAL

Chapter 9, Section D — Graphic Weather Products

GFD I/C VIDEO
Part III, Chapter 9, Section D

RECOMMENDED SEQUENCE:

1. Lesson Introduction and Video Presentation
2. Class Discussion

LESSON OBJECTIVES:

- Understand the information displayed on graphic weather products and how to use each product.

ACADEMIC CONTENT:

SECTION D — GRAPHIC WEATHER PRODUCTS

GRAPHIC REPORTS

❑ Surface Analysis Chart
❑ Weather Depiction Chart
❑ Radar Summary Chart
❑ Satellite Weather Pictures
❑ Composite Moisture Stability Chart
❑ Constant Pressure Analysis Chart
❑ Observed Winds and Temperature Aloft Chart

GRAPHIC FORECASTS

- ❑ Low-Level Significant Weather Prog
- ❑ High-Level Significant Weather Prog
- ❑ Convective Outlook Chart
- ❑ Forecast Winds and Temperatures Aloft Chart
- ❑ National Convective Weather Forecast
- ❑ Volcanic Ash Forecast Transport and Dispersion Chart

COMPLETION STANDARDS:

- Demonstrate ability to interpret and integrate information presented in graphic weather products during oral quizzing by instructor at completion of lesson.
- Student completes Chapter 9 questions for Section D with a minimum passing score of 80%, and the instructor reviews incorrect response to ensure complete understanding before the student progresses to Ground Lesson 23.

STUDY ASSIGNMENT:

INSTRUMENT/COMMERCIAL

Chapter 9, Section E — Sources of Weather Information

STAGE III GROUND LESSON 23

LESSON REFERENCES:

INSTRUMENT/COMMERCIAL

Chapter 9, Section E — Sources of Weather Information

GFD I/C VIDEO

Part III, Chapter 9, Section E

RECOMMENDED SEQUENCE:

1. Lesson Introduction and Video Presentation
2. Class Discussion

LESSON OBJECTIVES:

- Learn how to access preflight and in-flight sources of weather information.
- Learn how to interpret and use weather information for planning and in-flight purposes.

ACADEMIC CONTENT:

SECTION E — SOURCES OF WEATHER INFORMATION

PREFLIGHT WEATHER SOURCES

- ❑ Flight Service Station
- ❑ Preflight Weather Briefing
- ❑ Telephone Information Briefing Service
- ❑ Direct User Access Terminal System
- ❑ Private Industry Sources
- ❑ The World Wide Web

IN-FLIGHT WEATHER SOURCES

- ❑ Airmets and Sigmets
- ❑ Convective Sigmets
- ❑ Enroute Flight Advisory Service
- ❑ Flight Service Station
- ❑ Center Weather Advisories
- ❑ Hazardous In-Flight Weather Advisory Service
- ❑ Transcribed Weather Broadcasts
- ❑ Weather Radar Services
- ❑ Automated Surface Observing System
- ❑ Automated Weather Observing System

AIRBORNE WEATHER EQUIPMENT

- ❑ Weather Radar
- ❑ Lightning Detection Systems

COMPLETION STANDARDS:

- Demonstrate understanding of preflight and in-flight weather sources and their uses during oral quizzing by instructor at completion of lesson.
- Student completes Chapter 9 questions for Section E with a minimum passing score of 80%, and the instructor reviews incorrect responses to ensure complete understanding before the student progresses to Ground Lesson 24.

STUDY ASSIGNMENT:

INSTRUMENT/COMMERCIAL

Chapter 10, Section A — IFR Emergencies

STAGE III
GROUND LESSON 24

LESSON REFERENCES:

INSTRUMENT/COMMERCIAL

Chapter 10, Section A — IFR Emergencies

GFD I/C VIDEO

Part III, Chapter 10, Section A

RECOMMENDED SEQUENCE:

1. Lesson Introduction and Video Presentation
2. Class Discussion

LESSON OBJECTIVES:

- Learn to recognize emergency situations and perform the correct emergency procedures.

ACADEMIC CONTENT:

SECTION A — IFR EMERGENCIES

- ❑ Declaring an Emergency
- ❑ Minimum Fuel
- ❑ Gryoscopic Instrument Failure
- ❑ Communication Failure
- ❑ Emergency Approach Procedures
- ❑ Malfunction Reports

COMPLETION STANDARDS:

- Demonstrate ability to recognize and respond appropriately to emergency situations during oral quizzing by instructor at completion of lesson.
- Student completes Chapter 10 questions for Section A with a minimum passing score of 80%, and the instructor reviews incorrect responses to ensure complete understanding before the student progresses to Ground Lesson 25.

STUDY ASSIGNMENT:

INSTRUMENT/COMMERCIAL

Chapter 10, Section B — IFR Decision Making and Section C — IFR Flight Planning

STAGE III
GROUND LESSON 25

LESSON REFERENCES:

INSTRUMENT/COMMERCIAL

Chapter 10, Section B — IFR Decision Making and Section C — IFR Flight Planning

GFD I/C VIDEO

Part III, Chapter 10, Sections B and C

RECOMMENDED SEQUENCE:

1. Lesson Introduction and Video Presentation
2. Class Discussion

LESSON OBJECTIVES:

- Obtain the knowledge necessary to successfully plan an IFR flight and recognize the factors related to effective decision making.

ACADEMIC CONTENT:

SECTION B — IFR DECISION MAKING

❑ Decision-Making Process
❑ IFR Accident
❑ Poor Judgment Chain
❑ Assessing Risk
❑ Pilot-In-Command Responsibility
❑ Hazardous Attitudes
❑ Crew Relationships
❑ Communication
❑ Resource Use
❑ Workload Management
❑ Situational Awareness
❑ Controlled Flight Into Terrain

SECTION C — IFR FLIGHT PLANNING

❑ Route Selection
❑ Flight Information Publications
❑ Weather Considerations
❑ Altitude Selection
❑ Completing the Navigation Log
❑ Filing the Flight Plan
❑ Closing the IFR Flight Plan

COMPLETION STANDARDS:

- Demonstrate understanding of IFR flight planning and factors affecting the decision making process during oral quizzing by instructor at completion of lesson.
- Student completes Chapter 10 questions for Section B and C with a minimum passing score of 80%, and the instructor reviews incorrect responses to ensure complete understanding before the student progresses to Ground Lesson 26.

STUDY ASSIGNMENT:

INSTRUMENT/COMMERCIAL

Review Chapters 9 and 10 in preparation for the Stage III Exam.

STAGE III GROUND LESSON 26

STAGE III EXAM

LESSON REFERENCES:

INSTRUMENT/COMMERCIAL
Chapters 9 – 10

RECOMMENDED SEQUENCE:

1. Lesson Introduction
2. Testing
3. Critique

LESSON OBJECTIVES:

- Administer the stage exam to evaluate the student's comprehension of the information in Chapters 9 and 10 covering weather factors, weather hazards, and sources of weather information, as well as decision making, IFR flight planning, and emergency procedures.

ACADEMIC CONTENT:

STAGE III EXAM

- ❑ Meteorology
- ❑ IFR Flight Considerations

COMPLETION STANDARDS:

- The lesson and stage are complete when the student has completed the Stage III exam with a minimum passing score of 80%, and the instructor has reviewed each incorrect response to ensure complete understanding before the student progresses to the end-of-course exam.

STUDY ASSIGNMENT:

INSTRUMENT/COMMERCIAL
Review Chapters 1 – 10 in preparation for the Instrument Rating End-of-Course Exam.

STAGE III GROUND LESSON 27

END-OF-COURSE EXAM

LESSON REFERENCES:

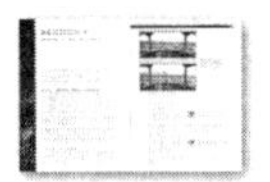
INSTRUMENT/COMMERCIAL
Chapters 1 – 10

FAR/AIM
Instrument FARs

GUIDED FLIGHT DISCOVERY TRAINING VIDEOS

RECOMMENDED SEQUENCE:

1. Lesson Introduction
2. Testing
3. Critique

LESSON OBJECTIVE:

- Administer and evaluate the students comprehension of academic material presented in Chapters 1 through 10 in preparation for the FAA instrument rating airmen knowledge test.

ACADEMIC CONTENT:

- ❑ Principles of Instrument Flight
- ❑ The Flight Environment
- ❑ Meteorology
- ❑ Departure Charts and Procedures
- ❑ Enroute Charts and Procedures
- ❑ Arrival Charts and Procedures
- ❑ Approach Charts and Procedures

COMPLETION STANDARDS:

- The lesson and stage are complete when the student has completed the Instrument Rating End-of-Course Exam with a minimum of 80%, and the instructor has reviewed each incorrect response to ensure complete understanding before the student progresses to the FAA instrument rating airmen knowledge test.

STUDY ASSIGNMENT:

Review the *Instrument/Commercial* textbook Chapters 1 – 10 in preparation for the FAA instrument rating airmen knowledge test.

INSTRUMENT RATING STAGE I

STAGE OBJECTIVES

The emphasis of Stage I is on IFR flight operations. The student will learn precise airplane attitude control by instrument reference. Additionally, the student will gain greater competence in the use of navigation systems.

STAGE COMPLETION STANDARDS

This stage is complete when the student can demonstrate precise airplane attitude control by instrument reference only. This will include the use of full and partial panel reference. In addition, the student will demonstrate accurate use of navigation systems by maintaining positional awareness at all times.

STAGE I FLIGHT LESSON 1

DUAL — LOCAL

RECOMMENDED SEQUENCE:

NOTE: *As indicated in the lesson Time Allocation tables, students should complete Ground Lessons 1, 2, and 3 prior to this flight.*

1. Preflight Orientation
2. Flight
3. Postflight Evaluation

LESSON OBJECTIVES:

- Become familiar with the instrument training airplane.
- Briefly review normal preflight, takeoff, and landing procedures.
- Practice attitude instrument flight with emphasis on precise aircraft control solely by instrument reference including basic instrument flight maneuvers.

REVIEW:

PREFLIGHT PREPARATION

- ❑ Aircraft Certificates and Documents
- ❑ Aircraft Logbooks
- ❑ Airworthiness Requirements
- ❑ Aircraft Performance
- ❑ Aircraft Weight and Balance
- ❑ Operation of Systems

NORMAL PROCEDURES

- ❑ Cockpit Resource Management
- ❑ Use of Checklists, distractions
- ❑ Positive Exchange of Flight Controls
- ❑ Engine Starting
- ❑ Collision Avoidance Procedures and CFIT
- ❑ Normal and Crosswind Taxiing
- ❑ Normal Takeoffs and Landings
- ❑ Crosswind Takeoffs and Landings
- ❑ Radio Communications and ATC Light Signals
- ❑ Aeronautical Decision Making, Judgment, Flight Scenarios, Risk Management
- ❑ Single-pilot Resource Management
- ❑ Runway Incursion
- ❑ Situational Awareness
- ❑ Security Checklist

INTRODUCE:

FULL PANEL INSTRUMENT

- ❑ Straight-and-Level Flight
- ❑ Standard-Rate Turns
- ❑ Constant Airspeed Climbs
- ❑ Climbing Turns
- ❑ Constant Airspeed Descents
- ❑ Descending Turns
- ❑ Power-Off Stalls
- ❑ Power-On Stalls
- ❑ Maneuvering During Slow Flight
- ❑ Recovery From Unusual Flight Attitudes
- ❑ Operations in Turbulence

COMPLETION STANDARDS:

- Takeoffs and landings will be conducted safely and at least at the private pilot proficiency level.
- During the flight the student will maintain altitude ±200 feet, heading ±15° and airspeed ±15 knots and bank angles within ±5° during turns.

POSTFLIGHT DISCUSSION AND PREVIEW OF NEXT LESSON

STAGE I FLIGHT LESSON 2

DUAL — LOCAL AIRPLANE OR PCATD

RECOMMENDED SEQUENCE:

1. Preflight Orientation
2. Flight
3. Postflight Evaluation

LESSON OBJECTIVES:

- Review full panel instrument flying in preparation for partial panel flight.
- Introduce the student to aircraft instrument systems, equipment, and preflight checks necessary for IFR flight.

REVIEW:

FULL PANEL INSTRUMENT

- ❑ Straight-and-Level Flight
- ❑ Standard-Rate Turns
- ❑ Constant Airspeed Climbs
- ❑ Constant Airspeed Descents

INTRODUCE:

- ❑ Aircraft Systems Related to IFR Operations
- ❑ Aircraft Flight Instruments and Navigation Equipment
- ❑ Preflight Check of Instruments, Equipment, and Systems
- ❑ Instrument Cockpit Check
- ❑ IFR Takeoff Preparations
- ❑ Change of Airspeed
- ❑ Steep Turns
- ❑ Checking Instruments and Equipment at Engine Shutdown
- ❑ Autopilot (if airplane so equipped)

COMPLETION STANDARDS:

- Demonstrate an understanding of and basic competence in full panel instrument attitude control.
- During the flight, the student will demonstrate understanding of aircraft attitude control by maintaining altitude ±200 feet, heading ±15° and airspeed ±15 knots.
- Display an understanding of the aircraft systems related to IFR operations and the importance of IFR takeoff preparations.

POSTFLIGHT DISCUSSION AND PREVIEW OF NEXT LESSON

STUDY ASSIGNMENT:

GROUND LESSON 4 —
Instrument Navigation

STAGE I FLIGHT LESSON 3

DUAL — LOCAL

RECOMMENDED SEQUENCE:

1. Preflight Orientation
2. Flight
3. Postflight Evaluation

LESSON OBJECTIVES:

- Review systems and equipment checks.
- Increase proficiency in full panel instrument flying.

REVIEW:

- ❑ Aircraft Systems Related to IFR Operations
- ❑ Aircraft Flight Instruments and Navigation Equipment
- ❑ Preflight Check of Instruments, Equipment, and Systems
- ❑ Instrument Cockpit Check
- ❑ Autopilot (if airplane so equipped)

FULL PANEL INSTRUMENT

- ❑ Straight-and-Level Flight
- ❑ Constant Airspeed Climbs
- ❑ Constant Airspeed Descents
- ❑ Change of Airspeed
- ❑ Standard-Rate Turns
- ❑ Power-Off Stalls
- ❑ Power-On Stalls
- ❑ Maneuvering During Slow Flight
- ❑ Recovery From Unusual Flight Attitudes
- ❑ Operations in Turbulence

COMPLETION STANDARDS:

- The student will exhibit a basic understanding of systems and equipment related to IFR operations.

- The student will precisely control the airplane using full panel instrument reference.
- With minor exceptions, the student should be able to maintain altitude ±200 feet, heading within ±15°, and airspeed within ±15 knots.
- Recognize the approach of stalls and demonstrate the correct recovery procedures from unusual flight attitudes.

POSTFLIGHT DISCUSSION AND PREVIEW OF NEXT LESSON

STAGE I
FLIGHT LESSON 4

DUAL — LOCAL

AIRPLANE OR PCATD

RECOMMENDED SEQUENCE:

1. Preflight Orientation
2. Flight
3. Postflight Evaluation

LESSON OBJECTIVES:

- Review full panel instrument flight.
- Introduce partial panel attitude instrument flying including related systems and equipment malfunctions.

REVIEW:

❑ IFR Aircraft Systems
❑ IFR Takeoff Preparations
❑ Steep Turns

INTRODUCE:

SYSTEMS AND EQUIPMENT MALFUNCTIONS

❑ Electrical System Failure
❑ Loss of Communications
❑ Vacuum Pump Failure
❑ Gyroscopic Instrument Failure

PARTIAL PANEL INSTRUMENT

❑ Straight-and-Level Flight
❑ Standard-Rate Turns
❑ Constant Airspeed Climbs
❑ Constant Airspeed Descents
❑ Change of Airspeed

COMPLETION STANDARDS:

- The student will begin to recognize and understand the effect of instrument systems and equipment malfunctions.
- Recognize the change in instrument cross-check necessary to maintain aircraft control while using partial panel procedures.

POSTFLIGHT DISCUSSION AND PREVIEW OF NEXT LESSON

STUDY ASSIGNMENT:

GROUND LESSONS 5 AND 6 —
Instrument FARs and Airports, Airspace, and Flight Information

---

STAGE I
FLIGHT LESSON 5
DUAL — LOCAL

RECOMMENDED SEQUENCE:

1. Preflight Orientation
2. Flight
3. Postflight Evaluation

LESSON OBJECTIVES:

- Continue to review full and partial panel instrument flight.
- Become more familiar with related systems and equipment malfunctions.
- Introduce additional full/partial panel instrument maneuvers and procedures.

REVIEW:

SYSTEMS AND EQUIPMENT MALFUNCTIONS

- ❑ Primary Flight Instrument Indicators Failure
- ❑ Loss of Communications Equipment

FULL AND PARTIAL PANEL INSTRUMENT

- ❑ Straight-and-Level Flight
- ❑ Standard-Rate Turns
- ❑ Steep Turns
- ❑ Constant Airspeed Climbs
- ❑ Constant Airspeed Descents
- ❑ Maneuvering During Slow Flight
- ❑ Power-Off Stalls
- ❑ Power-On Stalls

INTRODUCE:

FULL PANEL INSTRUMENT

- ❑ Constant Rate Climbs
- ❑ Constant Rate Descents
- ❑ Timed Turns to Magnetic Compass Headings

PARTIAL PANEL INSTRUMENT

- ❑ Recovery From Unusual Flight Attitudes
- ❑ Timed Turns to Magnetic Compass Headings
- ❑ Magnetic Compass Turns
- ❑ Constant Rate Climbs
- ❑ Constant Rate Descents

COMPLETION STANDARDS:

- Using partial panel instrument reference, the student will maintain altitude ±200 feet, heading ±15°, airspeed ±15 knots, and desired climb and descent rate ±150 feet per minute.
- Demonstrate a basic understanding of IFR systems operation and recognize systems and equipment malfunctions.

POSTFLIGHT DISCUSSION AND PREVIEW OF NEXT LESSON

STAGE I
FLIGHT LESSON 6
DUAL — LOCAL

RECOMMENDED SEQUENCE:

1. Preflight Orientation
2. Flight
3. Postflight Evaluation

LESSON OBJECTIVES:

- Further develop full and partial panel instrument attitude flying skills.
- Introduce partial panel stalls and maneuvering during slow flight.

REVIEW:

FULL AND PARTIAL PANEL INSTRUMENT

- ❑ Straight-and-Level Flight
- ❑ Constant Rate Climbs
- ❑ Constant Airspeed Climbs
- ❑ Constant Rate Descents
- ❑ Constant Airspeed Descents
- ❑ Timed Turns to Magnetic Compass Headings
- ❑ Magnetic Compass Turns
- ❑ Recovery From Unusual Flight Attitudes
- ❑ Postflight Instrument and Equipment Check

INTRODUCE:

PARTIAL PANEL INSTRUMENT

- ❑ Power-Off Stalls
- ❑ Power-On Stalls
- ❑ Maneuvering During Slow Flight

COMPLETION STANDARDS:

- Using partial panel and full panel instrument reference, the student will recognize the typical indications of stalls, as well as perform recoveries without abrupt control usage.
- The student will perform correct recovery techniques from unusual attitudes, using full and partial panel instrument reference.

POSTFLIGHT DISCUSSION AND PREVIEW OF NEXT LESSON

STUDY ASSIGNMENT:

GROUND LESSON 7 —
Air Traffic Control Systems

STAGE I
FLIGHT LESSON 7

DUAL — LOCAL

RECOMMENDED SEQUENCE:

1. Preflight Orientation
2. Flight
3. Postflight Evaluation

LESSON OBJECTIVES:

- Enhance proficiency in the listed full panel attitude instrument maneuvers.
- Improve partial panel skills in stall recoveries, slow flight, and unusual attitude recoveries.

REVIEW:

FULL PANEL INSTRUMENT

- ❑ Straight-and-Level Flight
- ❑ Standard-Rate Turns
- ❑ Constant Rate Climbs
- ❑ Constant Airspeed Climbs
- ❑ Constant Rate Descents
- ❑ Constant Airspeed Descents
- ❑ Power-Off Stalls
- ❑ Power-On Stalls
- ❑ Recovery From Unusual Flight Attitudes
- ❑ Steep Turns

PARTIAL PANEL INSTRUMENT

- ❑ Power-Off Stalls
- ❑ Power-On Stalls
- ❑ Maneuvering During Slow Flight
- ❑ Recovery From Unusual Flight Attitudes

COMPLETION STANDARDS:

- Using full panel instrument reference, the student will maintain altitude ±150 feet, heading ±10°, airspeed ±15 knots, and desired descent and climb rate ±100 feet per minute.
- The student will perform correct recovery techniques from unusual attitudes using full and partial panel instrument reference.
- The student will use recovery techniques from stalls using positive control techniques with a minimum loss of altitude.

POSTFLIGHT DISCUSSION AND PREVIEW OF NEXT LESSON

STUDY ASSIGNMENT:

GROUND LESSON 8 —
Air Traffic Control Clearances

STAGE I
FLIGHT LESSON 8
DUAL — LOCAL
AIRPLANE OR PCATD

RECOMMENDED SEQUENCE:

1. Preflight Orientation
2. Flight
3. Postflight Evaluation

LESSON OBJECTIVES:

- Continue to develop proficiency in the basic listed attitude instrument maneuvers.
- Gain an understanding of VOR orientation as well as VOR radial interception and tracking.

REVIEW:

FULL AND PARTIAL PANEL INSTRUMENT

- ❏ Straight-and-Level Flight
- ❏ Standard-Rate Turns
- ❏ Constant Rate Climbs
- ❏ Constant Airspeed Climbs
- ❏ Constant Rate Descents
- ❏ Constant Airspeed Descents
- ❏ Recovery From Unusual Flight Attitudes

INTRODUCE:

- ❏ VOR Accuracy Test
- ❏ VOR Orientation
- ❏ VOR Radial Interception and Tracking

COMPLETION STANDARDS:

- Using full panel instrument reference, the student will maintain altitude ±100 feet, heading ±10°, airspeed ±15 knots, and desired descent and climb rate ±100 feet per minute.
- During partial panel procedures, the student will maintain altitude ±100 feet, heading ±15°, airspeed ±15 knots, and desired descent and climb rate ±100 feet per minute.
- The student will perform correct recovery techniques from unusual attitudes using full and partial panel instrument reference.
- Display basic knowledge of VOR interception and radial tracking.

POSTFLIGHT DISCUSSION AND PREVIEW OF NEXT LESSON

STUDY ASSIGNMENT:

GROUND LESSON 9 —

Review, as necessary, for the Stage I Exam.

STAGE I
FLIGHT LESSON 9
DUAL — LOCAL

RECOMMENDED SEQUENCE:

1. Preflight Orientation
2. Flight
3. Postflight Evaluation

LESSON OBJECTIVES:

- The student will gain additional experience and knowledge understanding of VOR orientation, radial interception and tracking.
- Introduce VOR time and distance calculations, intercepting and tracking DME arcs (if the airplane is so equipped), and the use of ADF equipment and NDB procedures.

REVIEW:

- ❏ VOR Orientation
- ❏ VOR Radial Interception and Tracking

INTRODUCE:

- ❏ VOR Time, Speed, and Distance
- ❏ Intercepting and Tracking DME Arcs (If Airplane So Equipped)
- ❏ NDB Orientation and Homing
- ❏ NDB Bearing Interception and Tracking

COMPLETION STANDARDS:

- The student will maintain altitude ±100 feet, heading ±10°, airspeed ±15 knots, and desired descent and climb rate ±100 feet per minute while performing the listed procedures.
- The student will demonstrate increased competency in basic VOR procedures and begin to understand ADF equipment and NDB procedures.

POSTFLIGHT DISCUSSION AND PREVIEW OF NEXT LESSON

STAGE I FLIGHT LESSON 10

DUAL — LOCAL

AIRPLANE OR PCATD

RECOMMENDED SEQUENCE:

1. Preflight Orientation
2. Flight
3. Postflight Evaluation

LESSON OBJECTIVES:

- Practice and gain proficiency in VOR orientation, tracking, and time, speed, and distance calculations.
- Become familiar with basic ADF equipment and NDB procedures.
- Introduce NDB time, speed, and distance calculations.

REVIEW:

❑ VOR Orientation
❑ VOR Tracking
❑ VOR Time, Speed, and Distance
❑ Intercepting and Tracking DME Arcs (If Airplane So Equipped)
❑ NDB Orientation and Homing
❑ NDB Bearing Interception and Tracking

INTRODUCE:

❑ NDB Time, Speed, and Distance

COMPLETION STANDARDS:

- The student will demonstrate increased proficiency in all VOR procedures.
- The student will exhibit understanding of basic NDB procedures.

POSTFLIGHT DISCUSSION AND PREVIEW OF NEXT LESSON

STAGE I FLIGHT LESSON 11

DUAL — LOCAL

RECOMMENDED SEQUENCE:

1. Preflight Orientation
2. Flight
3. Postflight Evaluation

LESSON OBJECTIVES:

- Introduce front and back course localizer tracking.
- Continue to gain proficiency with full and partial panel procedures.
- Learn to interpret the CDI indications associated with the increased sensitivity of the localizer while tracking inbound on the front or back course.

REVIEW:

PARTIAL PANEL INSTRUMENT

❑ Straight-and-Level Flight
❑ Constant Rate Climbs
❑ Constant Airspeed Climbs
❑ Constant Rate Descents

- ❑ Constant Airspeed Descents
- ❑ Timed Turns to Magnetic Compass Headings

FULL PANEL INSTRUMENT

- ❑ VOR Tracking
- ❑ VOR Time and Distance
- ❑ Intercepting and Tracking DME Arcs (If Airplane So Equipped)

INTRODUCE:

- ❑ Localizer Tracking (Front Course)
- ❑ Localizer Tracking (Back Course)

COMPLETION STANDARDS:

- The student will demonstrate increased proficiency in full panel and partial panel VOR procedures.
- The student should maintain heading ±10° and altitude ±100 feet.
- The student will begin to understand localizer tracking.

POSTFLIGHT DISCUSSION AND PREVIEW OF NEXT LESSON

STAGE I
FLIGHT LESSON 12
DUAL — LOCAL

RECOMMENDED SEQUENCE:

1. Preflight Orientation
2. Flight
3. Postflight Evaluation

LESSON OBJECTIVES:

- Increase proficiency in basic attitude instrument flight procedures.
- Introduce VOR and NDB orientation/tracking procedures using partial panel.

REVIEW:

FULL PANEL INSTRUMENT

- ❑ Straight-and-Level Flight
- ❑ Standard-Rate Turns
- ❑ Climbs
- ❑ Descents
- ❑ Power-Off Stalls
- ❑ Power-On Stalls
- ❑ Recovery From Unusual Flight Attitudes
- ❑ Steep Turns

PARTIAL PANEL INSTRUMENT

- ❑ Timed Turns to Magnetic Compass Headings
- ❑ Magnetic Compass Turns
- ❑ Straight-and-Level Flight
- ❑ Standard-Rate Turns
- ❑ Climbs
- ❑ Descents
- ❑ Power-Off Stalls
- ❑ Power-On Stalls
- ❑ Recovery From Unusual Flight Attitudes

INTRODUCE:

PARTIAL PANEL INSTRUMENT

- ❑ Maneuvering During Slow Flight
- ❑ VOR Orientation
- ❑ VOR Tracking
- ❑ NDB Orientation
- ❑ NDB Tracking

COMPLETION STANDARDS:

- The student will demonstrate accurate VOR and NDB orientation in full panel and partial panel situations.
- Using partial panel and full panel instrument reference, the student will maintain altitude ±100 feet, heading ±10°, airspeed ±15 knots, and desired descent and climb rate ±100 feet per minute.
- The student will perform correct recovery techniques from unusual attitudes using full and partial panel instrument reference.
- The student will demonstrate the correct recovery techniques from stalls using positive control techniques with a minimum loss of altitude.

POSTFLIGHT DISCUSSION AND PREVIEW OF NEXT LESSON

STUDY ASSIGNMENT:

Review, as required, in preparation for the Stage I Check in Flight Lesson 13.

STAGE I FLIGHT LESSON 13

DUAL — LOCAL

STAGE I CHECK

RECOMMENDED SEQUENCE:

1. Preflight Orientation
2. Flight
3. Postflight Evaluation

LESSON OBJECTIVES:

- The chief instructor, assistant chief, or a designated check instructor will evaluate the student's proficiency in attitude instrument flight and navigation to ensure the student is prepared for more complex instrument flying procedures.

REVIEW:

FULL PANEL INSTRUMENT

- ❑ Straight-and-Level Flight
- ❑ Constant Rate Climbs
- ❑ Constant Airspeed Climbs
- ❑ Constant Rate Descents
- ❑ Constant Airspeed Descents
- ❑ Steep Turns
- ❑ Standard-Rate Turns
- ❑ Recovery From Unusual Flight Attitudes

PARTIAL PANEL INSTRUMENT

- ❑ Recovery From Unusual Flight Attitudes
- ❑ Timed Turns to Magnetic Compass Headings
- ❑ Magnetic Compass Turns
- ❑ Power-Off Stalls
- ❑ Power-On Stalls

INSTRUMENT NAVIGATION

- ❑ VOR Orientation
- ❑ VOR Tracking
- ❑ NDB Orientation
- ❑ NDB Tracking
- ❑ Time, Speed, and Distance Calculations
- ❑ Localizer Tracking

COMPLETION STANDARDS:

- The student will demonstrate accurate VOR and NDB orientation and tracking at all times.
- The student will perform correct recovery techniques from unusual attitudes using full and partial panel instrument reference.
- The student will use recovery techniques from stalls using positive control techniques with a minimum loss of altitude.
- Using full panel and partial panel instrument reference, the student will maintain altitude ±100 feet, heading ±10°, airspeed ±15 knots, and desired descent and climb rate ±100 feet per minute.

POSTFLIGHT DISCUSSION AND PREVIEW OF NEXT LESSON

STUDY ASSIGNMENT:

GROUND LESSONS 10, 11, AND 12 — Departure Charts and Departure Procedures, Enroute Charts and Procedures, and Holding Procedures

STAGE II

STAGE OBJECTIVES

The objective of Stage II is to introduce and train the student on holding patterns and instrument approaches, including circling and missed approach procedures. The student will learn to correctly perform holding patterns and accurate instrument approaches using full and partial panel techniques.

STAGE COMPLETION STANDARDS

This stage is complete when the student can demonstrate accuracy and proficiency in holding patterns and all required instrument approach procedures.

STAGE II FLIGHT LESSON 14

DUAL — LOCAL

AIRPLANE OR PCATD

RECOMMENDED SEQUENCE:

1. Preflight Orientation
2. Flight
3. Postflight Evaluation

LESSON OBJECTIVES:

- Review instrument systems and equipment malfunctions.
- The student should become familiar with VOR standard and nonstandard holding patterns, as well as standard NDB holding procedures.

REVIEW:

❏ Systems and Equipment Malfunctions
❏ Full Panel Instrument Flight

INTRODUCE:

VOR HOLDING

❏ Standard Holding
❏ Nonstandard Holding

NDB HOLDING

❏ Standard Holding

COMPLETION STANDARDS:

- The student will demonstrate a basic understanding and proficiency in VOR and NDB holding pattern procedures.
- The student should maintain orientation at all times during both standard and nonstandard VOR holding procedures.
- Exhibit basic understanding and skill in standard NDB holding procedures.

POSTFLIGHT DISCUSSION AND PREVIEW OF NEXT LESSON

STAGE II FLIGHT LESSON 15

DUAL — LOCAL

RECOMMENDED SEQUENCE:

1. Preflight Orientation
2. Flight
3. Postflight Evaluation

LESSON OBJECTIVES:

- The student should demonstrate increased proficiency in performing standard VOR and NDB holding patterns.
- Introduce nonstandard NDB and standard localizer holding procedures.

REVIEW:

❑ Standard VOR Holding
❑ Nonstandard VOR Holding
❑ Standard NDB Holding
❑ Localizer Tracking

INTRODUCE:

❑ Nonstandard NDB Holding
❑ Standard Localizer Holding

COMPLETION STANDARDS:

- The student will demonstrate the necessary skill and knowledge to perform the correct holding pattern entries and procedures for standard and nonstandard VOR holding patterns as well as standard NDB holding patterns.
- The student will exhibit basic understanding and ability to fly nonstandard NDB and localizer holding patterns using the appropriate entry, timing, and wind correction procedures.

POSTFLIGHT DISCUSSION AND PREVIEW OF NEXT LESSON

STAGE II FLIGHT LESSON 16

DUAL — LOCAL

RECOMMENDED SEQUENCE:

1. Preflight Orientation
2. Flight
3. Postflight Evaluation

LESSON OBJECTIVES:

- The student will review the holding procedures introduced in previous lessons.
- The student will also be introduced to other types of holding patterns.

REVIEW:

❑ Standard NDB Holding
❑ Nonstandard NDB Holding
❑ Standard Localizer Holding

INTRODUCE:

❑ Nonstandard Localizer Holding
❑ DME Holding (If Airplane So Equipped)
❑ Intersection Holding

COMPLETION STANDARDS:

- The student will exhibit the ability to perform the correct entry procedures for intersection and DME holding patterns (if the airplane is so equipped).
- The student should maintain the desired altitude ±100 feet,. assigned airspeed ±10 knots and headings ±10°, within 3/4 scale deflection of the CDI during the hold.

POSTFLIGHT DISCUSSION AND PREVIEW OF NEXT LESSON

STUDY ASSIGNMENT:

GROUND LESSONS 13, 14, 15, AND 16 — Arrival Charts, Arrival Procedures, Approach Charts, Nonprecision (NPA) Approach Procedures, and VOR and NDB Approaches
The student also should prepare for the IFR Approaches Briefing to be conducted prior to Flight Lesson 17.

STAGE II
FLIGHT LESSON 17
DUAL — LOCAL

RECOMMENDED SEQUENCE:

1. Preflight Orientation: Briefing — IFR Approaches
2. Flight
3. Postflight Evaluation

LESSON OBJECTIVES:

- Review previously learned holding pattern procedures and systems/equipment malfunctions.
- Familiarize the student with nonprecision instrument approach procedures (IAPs) and missed approach planning.

Note: *The instructor and student must keep in mind FAR 61.1(b)(9) which states an instrument approach means an approach procedure defined in Part 97 of the Federal Aviation Regulations.*

If the training airplane is DME-equipped, the syllabus listings for VOR approaches may include VORTAC approaches or VOR-DME approaches.

REVIEW:

- ❑ Holding Procedures
- ❑ Nonstandard NDB Holding
- ❑ Standard Localizer Holding
- ❑ Systems and Equipment Malfunction

INTRODUCE:

- ❑ VOR Approaches
- ❑ Localizer Approaches (Front Course)
- ❑ Approach Procedures to Straight-In Landing Minimums
- ❑ Missed Approach Procedures

COMPLETION STANDARDS:

- Demonstrate proficiency in the review maneuvers and procedures.
- The student also should be able to:
  1. Explain and use the information displayed on the approach charts.
  2. Execute several initial and intermediate approach segments to arrive at the final approach fix.
  3. Complete the final approach and let down to the missed approach fix.
  4. Demonstrate the missed approach procedure as appropriate to the published chart used.

POSTFLIGHT DISCUSSION AND PREVIEW OF NEXT LESSON

STAGE II
FLIGHT LESSON 18 AND 19
DUAL — LOCAL
AIRPLANE OR PCATD

RECOMMENDED SEQUENCE:

1. Preflight Orientation
2. Flight
3. Postflight Evaluation

LESSON OBJECTIVES:

- Begin to develop proficiency in nonprecision instrument approach procedures and missed approach planning.
- Introduce procedures for completing a circling approach and landing from a straight-in or circling approach.

REVIEW:

- ❑ VOR Approaches
- ❑ Front Course Localizer Approach
- ❑ Approach Procedures to Straight-In Landing Minimums
- ❑ Missed Approach Procedures

INTRODUCE:

- ❑ NDB Approaches
- ❑ Back Course Localizer Approach
- ❑ Approach Procedures to Circling Landing Minimums
- ❑ Landing From a Straight-In or Circling Approach Procedure
- ❑ Visual Descent Point
- ❑ Land and Hold Short Operations

COMPLETION STANDARDS:

- The student will maintain an altitude of ±200 feet on the initial and intermediate approach segments.
- On the final approach segment the student should maintain heading ±10° and allow less than 3/4 scale deflection of the CDI, airspeed ±10 knots, and altitude that is not more than 100 feet above and 0 feet below the MDA.

POSTFLIGHT DISCUSSION AND PREVIEW OF NEXT LESSON

STUDY ASSIGNMENT:

GROUND LESSON 17 —
ILS Approaches

STAGE II
FLIGHT LESSON 20

DUAL — LOCAL

AIRPLANE OR PCATD

RECOMMENDED SEQUENCE:

1. Preflight Orientation
2. Flight
3. Postflight Evaluation

LESSON OBJECTIVES:

- Improve proficiency in localizer and VOR approaches.
- Become familiar with ILS approach procedures.

REVIEW:

❑ Intercepting and Tracking DME Arcs (If Airplane So Equipped)
❑ VOR Approaches
❑ Localizer Approaches (Front and Back Course)
❑ Missed Approach Procedures

INTRODUCE:

❑ Precision Approach (PA) Procedures
❑ ILS Approaches

COMPLETION STANDARDS:

- The student should exhibit knowledge of front and back course localizer tracking while maintaining specific descent rates and altitudes.
- During ILS approaches, the student should demonstrate glide slope bracketing, using attitude changes to control airspeed and descent rates.

POSTFLIGHT DISCUSSION AND PREVIEW OF NEXT LESSON

STAGE II
FLIGHT LESSON 21

DUAL — LOCAL

RECOMMENDED SEQUENCE:

1. Preflight Orientation
2. Flight
3. Postflight Evaluation

LESSON OBJECTIVES:

- Review full panel instrument approach procedures for precision and nonprecision approaches.
- Introduce the student to the procedure for an approach with a loss of the primary flight instrument indicators.
- Introduce the student to no-gyro radar vectoring and approach procedures.

REVIEW:

❑ Full Panel Instrument (As necessary)
❑ ILS Approaches
❑ Localizer Approaches
❑ NDB Approaches
❑ Landing From a Straight-In or Circling Approach Procedure
❑ Intercepting and Tracking DME Arcs (If Airplane So Equipped)

INTRODUCE:

- ❏ Approach with loss of Primary Flight Instrument Indicators
- ❏ Missed Approach Procedure with loss of Primary Flight Instrument Indicators

COMPLETION STANDARDS:

- During the ILS approaches, the student should demonstrate accurate localizer interception and tracking and make a transition to the glide slope at the correct point.
- The glide slope and localizer should be maintained with no more than three quarter-scale needle deflection
- During the non-precision approaches, the student should maintain an altitude ±200 feet on the initial and intermediate approach segments.
- On the final approach segment, the student should maintain an altitude that is not more than 100 feet above the MDA.
- The student will exhibit understanding of the procedures used to perform no-gyro radar vectoring and approaches.

POSTFLIGHT DISCUSSION AND PREVIEW OF NEXT LESSON

STUDY ASSIGNMENT:

GROUND LESSON 18 —
GPS and VOR/DME RNAV Approaches
Begin to review, as needed, for the Stage II Check in Flight Lesson 23.

STAGE II
FLIGHT LESSON 22
DUAL — LOCAL, AIRPLANE OR PCATD

RECOMMENDED SEQUENCE:

1. Preflight Orientation
2. Flight
3. Postflight Evaluation

LESSON OBJECTIVES:

- The student should review instrument approach procedures as well as holding pattern entries and procedures in preparation for the stage exam.
- Introduce VOR/DME RNAV, GPS, and Approach with Vertical Guidance (APV) approach procedures (If Airplane So Equipped).

REVIEW:

- ❏ Standard VOR Holding
- ❏ Nonstandard VOR Holding
- ❏ Standard NDB Holding
- ❏ Nonstandard NDB Holding
- ❏ Standard Localizer Holding
- ❏ VOR, ILS, NDB Approaches
- ❏ No-Gyro Radar Vectoring and Approach Procedures
- ❏ Approach with loss of Primary Flight Instrument Indicators
- ❏ Missed Approach Procedure

INTRODUCE:

- ❏ RNAV Approach Procedures (If Airplane So Equipped)
- ❏ Approach with Vertical Guidance (APV) (If Airplane So Equipped)

COMPLETION STANDARDS:

- The student will demonstrate the ability to perform no-gyro radar approaches accurately.
- The student will demonstrate proficiency in the listed maneuvers in preparation for the Stage II Check.

POSTFLIGHT DISCUSSION AND PREVIEW OF NEXT LESSON

STUDY ASSIGNMENT:

GROUND LESSON 19 —
Review, as necessary, for the Stage II Exam.
Prepare for the Stage II Check in Flight Lesson 23.

STAGE II
FLIGHT LESSON 23

DUAL — LOCAL

STAGE II CHECK

RECOMMENDED SEQUENCE:

1. Preflight Orientation
2. Flight
3. Postflight Evaluation

LESSON OBJECTIVES:

- The chief instructor, assistant chief, or a designated check instructor will evaluate the student's proficiency in the proper execution of holding patterns and instrument approach procedures.

REVIEW:

- ❑ VOR Holding
- ❑ NDB Holding
- ❑ VOR Time and Distance
- ❑ Intercepting and Tracking DME Arcs (If Airplane So Equipped)
- ❑ VOR Approaches
- ❑ NDB Approaches
- ❑ ILS Approaches
- ❑ RNAV and APV Procedures (If Airplane So Equipped)
- ❑ Approach Procedures to Circling Landing Minimums
- ❑ Approach Procedures to Straight-In Landing Minimums
- ❑ Missed Approach Procedures
- ❑ Approach with loss of Primary Flight Instrument Indicators
- ❑ Land and Hold Short Operations

COMPLETION STANDARDS:

- The student should demonstrate instrument pilot proficiency, as outlined in the current FAA Instrument Rating Practical Test Standard, in each of the listed procedures.

POSTFLIGHT DISCUSSION AND PREVIEW OF NEXT LESSON

STUDY ASSIGNMENT:

GROUND LESSON 20 —
Weather Factors and Hazards
Prepare for the IFR Cross-Country Briefing to be conducted prior to Flight Lesson 24.

STAGE III

STAGE OBJECTIVES

The objective of Stage III is to introduce the student to IFR cross-country procedures and to increase the student's proficiency to the level required of an instrument rated pilot.

STAGE COMPLETION STANDARDS

This stage is complete when the student can demonstrate all IFR maneuvers and procedures at the proficiency level of an instrument rated pilot, as outlined in the current FAA Instrument Rating Practical Test Standards.

STAGE III FLIGHT LESSON 24

DUAL — CROSS-COUNTRY

AIRPLANE OR PCATD

RECOMMENDED SEQUENCE:

1. Preflight Orientation: Briefing — IFR Cross-Country
2. Flight
3. Postflight Evaluation

LESSON OBJECTIVES:

- The student should be introduced to IFR cross-country procedures by conducting an IFR cross-country over 50 nautical miles from the original point of departure with an emphasis on planning and departure procedures.
- The student should develop an understanding of the appropriate emergency procedures for enroute IFR operations.

REVIEW:

- ❑ Localizer Tracking
- ❑ Localizer Approaches
- ❑ ILS Approaches (As Needed)
- ❑ NDB Approaches (As Needed)
- ❑ VOR Approaches (As Needed)
- ❑ Loss Of Communications
- ❑ Loss of Attitude and/or Heading Indicator

INTRODUCE:

- ❑ IFR Cross-Country Flight Planning
- ❑ Weather Information Related to IFR Cross-Country Flight, IMC
- ❑ Aircraft Performance, Limitations, and Systems Related to IFR Cross Country
- ❑ Filing an IFR Flight Plan
- ❑ Departure Procedures and Clearances
- ❑ Air Traffic Control Clearance
- ❑ Clearance Copying
- ❑ Clearance Readback
- ❑ Use of SIDs and ODPs
- ❑ Use of Radar
- ❑ Voice Communications
- ❑ Enroute Procedures and Clearances
- ❑ Arrival Procedures and Clearances
- ❑ Canceling an IFR Flight Plan

SIMULATED EMERGENCY PROCEDURES

- ❑ Radio Failure
- ❑ Instrument Failure
- ❑ Systems Failure
- ❑ Equipment Failure
- ❑ Icing
- ❑ Turbulence
- ❑ Low Fuel Supply
- ❑ Engine Failure

COMPLETION STANDARDS:

- The student will exhibit knowledge of the procedures involved in cross-country planning, filing IFR flight plans, and obtaining IFR clearances.
- The student will demonstrate a basic understanding of the various simulated emergency procedures.

POSTFLIGHT DISCUSSION AND PREVIEW OF NEXT LESSON

STUDY ASSIGNMENT:

GROUND LESSON 22 —
Graphic Weather Products

STAGE III
FLIGHT LESSON 25
DUAL — CROSS-COUNTRY

RECOMMENDED SEQUENCE:

1. Preflight Orientation
2. Flight
3. Postflight Evaluation

LESSON OBJECTIVES:

- Introduce the student to IFR flight planning applications by conducting an IFR cross-country over 50 nautical miles from the original point of departure, becoming familiar with IFR departure, enroute, and arrival procedures.
- Review the appropriate emergency procedures for enroute IFR operations.

REVIEW:

❏ Weather Information Related to IFR Cross-Country
❏ Aircraft Performance, Limitations, and Systems Related to IFR Cross-Country
❏ Filing an IFR Flight Plan
❏ Departure Procedures and Clearances
❏ Air Traffic Control Clearances
❏ Use of SIDs and ODPs
❏ Use of Radar
❏ VOR Navigation
❏ Holding Procedures
❏ Simulated Emergency Procedures
❏ Enroute Procedures and Clearances
❏ Calculating ETEs and ETAs
❏ Enroute Course Changes
❏ Arrival Procedures and Clearances
❏ Use of STARs
❏ Use of Departure Radar

COMPLETION STANDARDS:

- The student will exhibit knowledge of the procedures involved in cross-country planning, filing IFR flight plans, and obtaining IFR clearances.
- Demonstrate a basic understanding of the various simulated emergency procedures.

POSTFLIGHT DISCUSSION AND PREVIEW OF NEXT LESSON

STUDY ASSIGNMENT:

GROUND LESSONS 23, 24, AND 25 —
Sources of Weather Information, IFR Emergencies, and IFR Decision Making/Flight Planning

---

STAGE III
FLIGHT LESSON 26
DUAL — CROSS-COUNTRY

RECOMMENDED SEQUENCE:

1. Preflight Orientation
2. Flight
3. Postflight Evaluation

LESSON OBJECTIVES:

- The student will continue to learn how to accurately plan and conduct an IFR cross-country flight and become more familiar with IFR departure, enroute, and arrival procedures.
- Introduce the student to aeronautical decision making and cockpit management concepts in the IFR environment.

NOTE: *The flight is designed to meet the cross-country requirements stated in FAR Part 141, Appendix C. It includes at least three different types of approaches using navigation systems, each approach executed at a different airport. The flight must be at least 250 nautical miles in length on federal airways or as routed by ATC. One leg of the flight must be at least 100 nautical miles in a straight line distance. The flight must also be conducted under IFR in the category and class of airplane for which the course is approved.*

REVIEW:

IFR CROSS-COUNTRY FLIGHT PLANNING

- ❑ Preflight Check of Instruments and Equipment Obtaining an IFR Clearance
- ❑ Filing an IFR Flight Plan
- ❑ Weather Information
- ❑ Aircraft Performance, Limitations, and Systems
- ❑ Departure Procedures and Clearances
- ❑ Use of SIDs and ODPs
- ❑ Use of Radar
- ❑ Enroute Procedures and Clearances
- ❑ VOR Navigation
- ❑ NDB Navigation
- ❑ Holding
- ❑ Enroute Course Changes
- ❑ Calculating ETEs and ETAs

SIMULATED EMERGENCY PROCEDURES

- ❑ Loss of Communications
- ❑ Loss of Attitude and/or Heading Indicator
- ❑ Other Systems Malfunctions
- ❑ Icing
- ❑ Turbulence
- ❑ Low Fuel Supply
- ❑ Engine Failure

ARRIVAL PROCEDURES AND CLEARANCES

- ❑ Use of STARs
- ❑ Use of Radar
- ❑ VOR Approach
- ❑ NDB Approach
- ❑ ILS Approach
- ❑ Approach Procedures to Circling Landing Minimums
- ❑ Missed Approach Procedures
- ❑ Aeronautical Decision Making and Judgment
- ❑ Cockpit Resource Management

COMPLETION STANDARDS:

- At the completion of this flight, the student should have a thorough understanding of cross-country and simulated emergency procedures appropriate to the aircraft to be used for the practical test.
- The student should have command of the airplane at all times during the flight, exercise sound judgment, and accurately comply with ATC procedures and clearances.

POSTFLIGHT DISCUSSION AND PREVIEW OF NEXT LESSON

STUDY ASSIGNMENT:

Prepare for the Instrument Rating Practical Test Briefing, to be conducted prior to Flight Lesson 27.

STAGE III

FLIGHT LESSON 27

DUAL — CROSS-COUNTRY

RECOMMENDED SEQUENCE:

1. Preflight Orientation: Briefing — Instrument Rating Practical Test
2. Flight
3. Postflight Evaluation

LESSON OBJECTIVES:

- Increase the students proficiency in planning and conducting all phases of the IFR cross-country flight in preparation for the Stage III Exam.
- The student should understand the appropriate emergency procedures as well as resource management and decision making practices for enroute IFR operations.
- Develop student competency in utilizing resource management and decision making skills.

REVIEW:

- ❑ Weather Information Related to IFR Cross-Country
- ❑ Aircraft Performance, Limitations, and Systems Related to IFR Cross-Country
- ❑ Cockpit Resource Management
- ❑ Filing an IFR Flight Plan
- ❑ Obtaining an IFR Clearance
- ❑ Clearance Copying

- ❑ Clearance Readback
- ❑ IFR Departure Procedures and Clearances
- ❑ IFR Enroute Procedures and Clearances
- ❑ IFR Approach Procedures and Clearances
- ❑ Canceling an IFR Flight Plan
- ❑ VOR Holding
- ❑ NDB Holding
- ❑ VOR Time and Distance
- ❑ VOR Approaches
- ❑ NDB Approaches
- ❑ ILS Approaches
- ❑ Missed Approach Procedures
- ❑ Partial Panel Nonprecision Instrument Approach Procedures
- ❑ Aeronautical Decision Making and Judgment

COMPLETION STANDARDS:

- The student should demonstrate instrument pilot knowledge and proficiency, as outlined in the current FAA Instrument Rating Practical Test Standards, in each of the listed procedures.

POSTFLIGHT DISCUSSION AND PREVIEW OF NEXT LESSON

STUDY ASSIGNMENT:

Prepare for the Stage III Exam in Ground Lesson 26. Begin a comprehensive review in preparation for the Instrument Rating End-of-Course Exam in Ground Lesson 27.

STAGE III
FLIGHT LESSON 28

DUAL — CROSS COUNTRY

STAGE III CHECK

RECOMMENDED SEQUENCE:

1. Preflight Orientation
2. Flight
3. Postflight Evaluation

LESSON OBJECTIVES:

- The chief instructor, assistant chief, or a designated check instructor will evaluate the student's IFR cross-country skills. This is the final stage check in preparation for the instrument rating practical test.

REVIEW:

IFR CROSS-COUNTRY FLIGHT PLANNING

- ❑ Filing an IFR Flight Plan
- ❑ IFR Preflight Inspection
- ❑ IFR Takeoff Preparations
- ❑ IFR Departure Procedures and Clearances
- ❑ Cockpit Resource Management
- ❑ Voice Communications

ARRIVAL PROCEDURES AND CLEARANCES

- ❑ ILS Approach
- ❑ VOR Approach
- ❑ NDB Approach
- ❑ Missed Approach Procedures
- ❑ Landing From a Straight-In or Circling Approach Procedure
- ❑ Aeronautical Decision Making and Judgment
- ❑ Land and Hold Short Operations

SIMULATED EMERGENCY PROCEDURES

- ❑ Loss of Communications
- ❑ Radio Failure
- ❑ Instrument Failure
- ❑ Equipment Failure
- ❑ Engine Failure
- ❑ Systems Failure

COMPLETION STANDARDS:

- The student should demonstrate complete understanding of IFR cross-country procedures.
- The student will perform all IFR and pertinent simulated emergency procedures at the instrument pilot proficiency level, as outlined in the current FAA instrument rating practical test standards.

POSTFLIGHT DISCUSSION AND PREVIEW OF NEXT LESSON

STUDY ASSIGNMENT:

GROUND LESSON 27 —
Review, as necessary, to prepare for the Instrument Rating End-of-Course Exam.

STAGE III
FLIGHT LESSON 29
DUAL — LOCAL
END-OF-COURSE
FLIGHT CHECK FOR
COURSE COMPLETION

RECOMMENDED SEQUENCE:

1. Preflight Orientation
2. Flight
3. Postflight Evaluation

LESSON OBJECTIVE:

- The chief instructor, assistant chief, or a designated check instructor will evaluate the student's IFR skills. This is the End-of-Course Check in preparation for the Instrument Rating Practical Test.

REVIEW:

- ❑ Cross-Country Planning
- ❑ Instrument Cockpit Check
- ❑ Air Traffic Control Clearances
- ❑ Emergency Procedures

FULL PANEL INSTRUMENT

- ❑ Straight and Level
- ❑ Constant Rate Climbs
- ❑ Constant Airspeed Climbs
- ❑ Constant Rate Descents
- ❑ Constant Airspeed Descents
- ❑ Standard-Rate Turns
- ❑ Steep Turns
- ❑ Recovery From Unusual Flight Attitudes

PARTIAL PANEL INSTRUMENT

- ❑ Recovery From Unusual Flight Attitudes
- ❑ Timed Turns to Magnetic Compass Headings
- ❑ Magnetic Compass Turns
- ❑ Power-Off Stalls
- ❑ Power-On Stalls

INSTRUMENT NAVIGATION

- ❑ VOR Orientation
- ❑ VOR Tracking
- ❑ NDB Orientation
- ❑ NDB Tracking
- ❑ Time, Speed, and Distance Calculations
- ❑ Localizer Tracking

VOR

- ❑ Orientation
- ❑ Radial Interception
- ❑ Tracking
- ❑ VOR Time and Distance
- ❑ VOR Approaches
- ❑ VOR Holding

NDB

- ❑ Orientation
- ❑ Radial Interception
- ❑ Tracking
- ❑ NDB Time and Distance
- ❑ NDB Approaches
- ❑ NDB Holding

PARTIAL PANEL INSTRUMENT

- ❑ Straight-and-Level Flight
- ❑ Standard Rate Turns
- ❑ Constant Rate Climbs and Descents
- ❑ Constant Airspeed Climbs and Descents
- ❑ Recovery From Unusual Flight Attitudes
- ❑ Nonprecision Instrument Approaches
- ❑ Time and Distance Calculations
- ❑ Intercepting and Tracking DME Arcs (If Airplane So Equipped)

OTHER INSTRUMENT PROCEDURES

- ❑ ILS Approaches
- ❑ Approach Procedures to Circling Landing Minimums
- ❑ Approach Procedures to Straight-In Landing Minimums
- ❑ Missed Approach Procedures
- ❑ Partial Panel Nonprecision Instrument Approach Procedures
- ❑ Aircraft Flight Instruments
- ❑ Navigation Equipment

- ❏ Timed Turns to Magnetic Compass Headings
- ❏ Magnetic Compass Turns
- ❏ RNAV Approaches (If Airplane So Equipped)

COMPLETION STANDARDS:

- The student will perform all IFR and pertinent simulated emergency procedures at the instrument pilot proficiency level, as outlined in the current FAA instrument rating practical test standards.

POSTFLIGHT DISCUSSION AND PREVIEW OF NEXT LESSON

COMMERCIAL PILOT CERTIFICATION STAGE IV

STAGE OBJECTIVES

During this stage, the student will review airports, airspace, flight information, and meteorology, as well as airplane performance, VFR cross-country planning, and navigation. In addition, the student will gain a greater understanding of aviation physiology, aeronautical decision making, and the FARs applicable to commercial pilot operations.

STAGE COMPLETION STANDARDS

This stage is complete when the student has taken the Stage IV Exam with a minimum passing score of 80%, and the instructor has reviewed each incorrect response to ensure complete understanding before the student progresses to Stage V.

NOTE: *Students not enrolled in the combined Instrument/Commercial Course should read Chapter 1, Section A — Instrument/Commercial Training and Opportunities prior to Ground Lesson 28.*

STAGE IV GROUND LESSON 28

LESSON REFERENCES:

INSTRUMENT/COMMERCIAL

Chapter 3, Section A — Airports, Airspace, and Flight Information

Chapter 9, Meteorology

NOTE: *Students enrolled in the combined Instrument/Commercial Course are not required to accomplish the review of Chapter 3, Section A — Airports, Airspace, and Flight Information and Chapter 9, Meteorology.*

SECTIONAL, TERMINAL, AND WORLD AERONAUTICAL CHARTS

GFD I/C VIDEO

Part I, Chapter 3, Section A
Part III, Chapter 9

RECOMMENDED SEQUENCE:

1. Lesson Introduction and Video Presentation
2. Class Discussion

LESSON OBJECTIVES:

- Review the airport environment, airspace, and flight information including collision avoidance and runway incursion avoidance.
- Review the weather patterns and hazards related to flight operations, the information contained in printed weather reports and forecasts and graphic weather products, as well as sources of weather information.
- Review and improve knowledge of aeronautical charts for operations under VFR.

ACADEMIC CONTENT:

CHAPTER 3, SECTION A — AIRPORTS, AIRSPACE AND FLIGHT INFORMATION

- ❑ Runway and Taxiway Markings
- ❑ Runway Incursion Avoidance
- ❑ Land and Hold Short Operations (LAHSO)
- ❑ Lighting Systems
- ❑ Airspace
- ❑ Flight Information

CHAPTER 9

- ❑ Weather Factors
- ❑ Weather Hazards
- ❑ Printed Reports and Forecasts
- ❑ Graphic Weather Products
- ❑ Sources of Weather Information

AERONAUTICAL CHARTS

- ❑ Sectional Charts
- ❑ VFR Terminal Area Charts
- ❑ World Aeronautical Charts

- ❏ Longitude and Latitude
- ❏ Airport Data
- ❏ Navigation Aids
- ❏ Airspace
- ❏ Obstructions
- ❏ Topographical Information

COMPLETION STANDARDS:

- Demonstrate understanding of the airport environment, airspace, and flight information during oral quizzing by the instructor at completion of lesson.
- Demonstrate understanding of weather factors, weather hazards, printed reports and forecasts, graphic weather products, and the sources of weather information during oral quizzing by instructor at completion of lesson.
- Student completes Chapter 3 questions for Section A and Chapter 9 questions with a minimum passing score of 80%, and the instructor reviews each incorrect response to ensure complete understanding before the student progresses to Ground Lesson 29.

NOTE: *Students enrolled in the combined Instrument/Commercial Course are not required to complete Chapter 3 questions for Section A and Chapter 9 questions.*

- Demonstrate understanding of VFR aeronautical charts used for cross-country flight during oral quizzing by instructor before the student progresses to Ground Lesson 29.

STUDY ASSIGNMENT:

Review pilotage and dead reckoning methods for VFR cross country.

STAGE IV GROUND LESSON 29

RECOMMENDED SEQUENCE:

1. Lesson Introduction
2. Class Discussion

LESSON OBJECTIVES:

- Review and improve the student's knowledge of pilotage and dead reckoning navigation under VFR.
- Become familiar with guidelines and recommended procedures related to flight planning, including proper VFR cruising altitudes, route selection based on airspace, and lost procedures.

ACADEMIC CONTENT:

PILOTAGE AND DEAD RECKONING

- ❏ Pilotage
- ❏ Selecting Checkpoints
- ❏ Following a Route
- ❏ Orientation
- ❏ Dead Reckoning
- ❏ Navigation Plotter
- ❏ Flight Planning
- ❏ Navigation Log
- ❏ Flight Plan
- ❏ Position Reports
- ❏ Flying Over Hazardous Terrain

COMPLETION STANDARDS:

- Demonstrate understanding of pilotage and dead reckoning methods for cross-country VFR flight during oral quizzing by instructor before the student progresses to Ground Lesson 30.

Review as necessary,

INSTRUMENT/COMMERCIAL

Chapter 1, Section B — Advanced Human Factors Concepts

STUDY ASSIGNMENT: STAGE IV GROUND LESSON 30

LESSON REFERENCES:

INSTRUMENT/COMMERCIAL

Chapter 1, Section B — Advanced Human Factors Concepts

RECOMMENDED SEQUENCE:

1. Lesson Introduction
2. Class Discussion

LESSON OBJECTIVES:

- During this lesson, the student will review and become more familiar with the common physiological factors affecting day and night flight operations.
- The student also will learn the common adverse effects of these physiological factors.

ACADEMIC CONTENT:

AVIATION PHYSIOLOGY

- ❏ The Eye
- ❏ Night Vision
- ❏ Night Scanning
- ❏ Visual Illusions
- ❏ Autokinesis
- ❏ Landing Illusions
- ❏ Flicker Vertigo
- ❏ Disorientation
- ❏ Illusions Leading to Disorientation
- ❏ Motion Sickness
- ❏ Respiration
- ❏ Hypoxia
- ❏ Prevention of Hypoxia
- ❏ Hyperventilation
- ❏ Decompression Sickness
- ❏ Alcohol, Drugs, and Performance

COMPLETION STANDARDS:

- Demonstrate knowledge of the physiological factors, especially vision, affecting the pilot in flight operations during oral quizzing by instructor before the student progresses to Ground Lesson 31.

STUDY ASSIGNMENT:

Review as necessary,

INSTRUMENT/COMMERCIAL

Chapter 1, Section B — Advanced Human Factors Concepts

STAGE IV GROUND LESSON 31

LESSON REFERENCES:

INSTRUMENT/COMMERCIAL

Chapter 1, Section B — Advanced Human Factors Concepts

RECOMMENDED SEQUENCE:

1. Lesson Introduction
2. Class Discussion

LESSON OBJECTIVES:

- During this lesson, the student will gain additional knowledge of the human factors concepts and crew resource management principles which affect aeronautical decision making and judgment.

ACADEMIC CONTENT:

AERONAUTICAL DECISION MAKING AND JUDGMENT

- ❏ Aeronautical Decision Making
- ❏ Crew Resource Management
- ❏ Decision-Making Process
- ❏ Pilot-in-Command Responsibility
- ❏ Hazardous Attitudes
- ❏ Communication
- ❏ Resource Use

❑ Workload Management
❑ Situational Awareness

COMPLETION STANDARDS:

- Demonstrate understanding of human factors concepts and crew resource management principles and their effect on flight safety during oral quizzing by instructor before progressing to Ground Lesson 32.

STUDY ASSIGNMENT:

FAR/AIM
Commercial FARs

STAGE IV
GROUND LESSON 32

LESSON REFERENCES:

FAR/AIM
Commercial FARs

RECOMMENDED SEQUENCE:

1. Lesson Introduction
2. Class Discussion

LESSON OBJECTIVES:

- Introduce FARs related specifically to commercial pilot operations.
- Review NTSB Part 830.

ACADEMIC CONTENT:

❑ FAR 1
❑ FAR 61
❑ FAR 91
❑ FAR 119
❑ NTSB Part 830

COMPLETION STANDARDS:

- Demonstrate understanding of the FARs and NTSB Part 830 during oral quizzing by instructor at completion of lesson.
- Student completes the Commercial Pilot (Airplane) Exercises in the FAR/AIM with a minimum passing score of 80%, and the instructor reviews incorrect responses to ensure complete understanding before the student progresses to the Stage IV Exam in Lesson 33.

STUDY ASSIGNMENT:

Review as necessary in preparation for the Stage IV Exam.

STAGE IV
GROUND LESSON 33

STAGE IV EXAM

LESSON REFERENCES:

INSTRUMENT/COMMERCIAL
Chapter 1, Section B; Chapter 3, Section A; Chapter 9

SECTIONAL, TERMINAL, AND WORLD AERONAUTICAL CHARTS

FAR/AIM
Commercial FARs

RECOMMENDED SEQUENCE:

1. Lesson Introduction
2. Testing
3. Critique

LESSON OBJECTIVES:

- Administer the Stage IV Exam covering the review of aeronautical charts and VFR cross-country operations, as well as sections of Chapters 1, 3, and 9 of the *Instrument/Commercial* textbook, and the commercial FARs.

ACADEMIC CONTENT:

STAGE IV EXAM

- ❑ Airports, Airspace, and Flight Information
- ❑ Meteorology
- ❑ Aeronautical Charts
- ❑ Pilotage and Dead Reckoning
- ❑ Aviation Physiology
- ❑ Aeronautical Decision Making and Judgment
- ❑ Commercial FARs and NTSB Part 830

COMPLETION STANDARDS:

- The lesson and stage are complete when the student has passed the Stage IV Exam with a minimum score of 80%, and the instructor has reviewed each incorrect response to ensure complete understanding before the student progresses to the next stage in Lesson 34.

STUDY ASSIGNMENT:

INSTRUMENT/COMMERCIAL

Chapter 11, Section A — High Performance Powerplants

STAGE V

STAGE OBJECTIVES

During this stage, the student will learn the operation of complex aircraft systems, how to predict aircraft performance, and advanced aerodynamics appropriate to complex airplanes. The student also will learn about commercial decision making, and how to perform the flight maneuvers required for commercial pilot certification.

STAGE COMPLETION STANDARDS

This stage is complete when the student has passed the Stage V Exam and the Commercial Pilot End-of-Course Exam with a minimum score of 80%, and the instructor has reviewed each incorrect response to ensure complete student understanding.

STAGE V

GROUND LESSON 34

LESSON REFERENCES:

INSTRUMENT/COMMERCIAL
Chapter 11, Section A — High Performance Powerplants

GFD I/C VIDEO
Part IV, Chapter 11, Section A

RECOMMENDED SEQUENCE:

1. Lesson Introduction and Video Presentation
2. Class Discussion

LESSON OBJECTIVES:

- Gain a working understanding of fuel injection systems including components and systems operation.
- Become familiar with high performance engine systems and their proper use.
- Understand the concepts and systems related to propeller pitch control.

ACADEMIC CONTENT:

SECTION A — HIGH PERFORMANCE POWERPLANTS

- ❑ Fuel Injection Systems
- ❑ Starting Procedures
- ❑ Normal Starts
- ❑ Hot Starts
- ❑ Flooded Starts
- ❑ Engine Monitoring
- ❑ Exhaust Gas Temperature Gauge
- ❑ Cylinder Head Temperature Gauge
- ❑ Abnormal Combustion
- ❑ Induction Icing

TURBOCHARGING

- ❑ Turbocharging Principles
- ❑ System Operation
- ❑ High Altitude Performance

CONSTANT-SPEED PROPELLERS

- ❑ Propeller Principles
- ❑ Constant-Speed Propeller Operation
- ❑ Power Controls

COMPLETION STANDARDS:

- Demonstrate understanding of high performance powerplants during oral quizzing by instructor at completion of lesson.
- Student completes Chapter 11 questions for Section A with a minimum passing score of 80%, and the instructor reviews incorrect responses to ensure complete understanding before the student progresses to Ground Lesson 35.

STUDY ASSIGNMENT:

INSTRUMENT/COMMERCIAL
Chapter 11, Section B — Environmental and Ice Control Systems

STAGE V
GROUND LESSON 35

LESSON REFERENCES:

INSTRUMENT/COMMERCIAL
Chapter 11, Section B — Environmental and Ice Control Systems

GFD I/C VIDEO
Part IV, Chapter 11, Section B

RECOMMENDED SEQUENCE:

1. Lesson Introduction and Video Presentation
2. Class Discussion

LESSON OBJECTIVES:

- Understand the operation of aircraft environmental control systems.
- Gain a working knowledge of the operation and limitations of ice control systems.

ACADEMIC CONTENT:

SECTION B — ENVIRONMENTAL AND ICE CONTROL SYSTEMS

OXYGEN SYSTEMS

❑ Continuous-Flow
❑ Diluter-Demand
❑ Pressure-Demand
❑ Oxygen Storage
❑ Oxygen Servicing

CABIN PRESSURIZATION

❑ Operating Principles
❑ Pressurization Principles
❑ Pressurization Components
❑ Pressurization Emergencies

ICE CONTROL SYSTEMS

❑ Airfoil Ice Control
❑ Windshield Ice Control
❑ Propeller Ice Control
❑ Other Ice Control Systems

COMPLETION STANDARDS:

- Demonstrate understanding of environmental and ice control systems during oral quizzing by instructor at completion of lesson.
- Student completes Chapter 11 questions for Section B with a minimum passing score of 80%, and the instructor reviews incorrect responses to ensure complete understanding before the student progresses to Ground Lesson 36.

STUDY ASSIGNMENT:

INSTRUMENT/COMMERCIAL
Chapter 11, Section C — Retractable Landing Gear

STAGE V
GROUND LESSON 36

LESSON REFERENCES:

INSTRUMENT/COMMERCIAL
Chapter 11, Section C — Retractable Landing Gear

GFD I/C VIDEO
Part IV, Chapter 11, Section C

RECOMMENDED SEQUENCE:

1. Lesson Introduction and Video Presentation
2. Class Discussion

LESSON OBJECTIVES:

- Understand the operation and limitations of retractable landing gear systems.

ACADEMIC CONTENT:

SECTION C — RETRACTABLE LANDING GEAR

- ❑ Landing Gear Systems
- ❑ Gear System Safety
- ❑ Airspeed Limitations
- ❑ Operating Procedures
- ❑ Gear System Malfunctions
- ❑ Emergency Gear Extension

COMPLETION STANDARDS:

- Demonstrate understanding of retractable landing gear systems during oral quizzing by instructor at completion of lesson.
- Student completes Chapter 11 questions for Section C with a minimum passing score of 80%, and the instructor reviews incorrect responses to ensure complete understanding before the student progresses to Ground Lesson 37.

STUDY ASSIGNMENT:

INSTRUMENT/COMMERCIAL
Chapter 12, Section A — Advanced Aerodynamics

STAGE V
GROUND LESSON 37

LESSON REFERENCES:

INSTRUMENT/COMMERCIAL
Chapter 12, Section A — Advanced Aerodynamics

SEQUENCE:

1. Lesson Introduction
2. Class Discussion

LESSON OBJECTIVES:

- Integrate aerodynamic theory with the operational factors affecting airplane flight characteristics.

ACADEMIC CONTENT:

SECTION A — ADVANCED AERODYNAMICS

FOUR FORCES OF FLIGHT

- ❑ Lift
- ❑ Lift Equation
- ❑ Controlling Lift
- ❑ High Lift Devices
- ❑ Drag
- ❑ Induced Drag
- ❑ Parasite Drag
- ❑ Ground Effect
- ❑ Thrust
- ❑ Weight and Load Factor
- ❑ V-g Diagram

AIRCRAFT STABILITY

- ❑ Static
- ❑ Dynamic
- ❑ Longitudinal Stability
- ❑ Lateral Stability
- ❑ Directional Stability

AERODYNAMICS AND FLIGHT MANEUVERS

- ❑ Straight-and-Level Flight
- ❑ Climbs
- ❑ Glides
- ❑ Turns
- ❑ Stall and Spin Awareness
- ❑ Stall Causes and Types
- ❑ Stall Recognition and Recovery
- ❑ Spin Causes and Phases
- ❑ Spin Recovery

COMPLETION STANDARDS:

- Demonstrate understanding of advanced aerodynamic concepts during oral quizzing by instructor at completion of lesson.
- Student completes Chapter 12 questions for Section A with a minimum passing score of 80%, and the instructor reviews incorrect responses to ensure complete understanding before the student progresses to Ground Lesson 38.

STUDY ASSIGNMENT:

INSTRUMENT/COMMERCIAL

Chapter 12, Section B — Predicting Performance

STAGE V
GROUND LESSON 38

LESSON REFERENCES:

INSTRUMENT/COMMERCIAL

Chapter 12, Section B — Predicting Performance

RECOMMENDED SEQUENCE:

1. Lesson Introduction
2. Class Discussion

LESSON OBJECTIVES:

- Gain the working knowledge needed to understand airplane performance and the methods used to calculate performance.

ACADEMIC CONTENT:

SECTION B — PREDICTING PERFORMANCE

FACTORS AFFECTING PERFORMANCE

- ❑ Density Altitude
- ❑ Surface Winds
- ❑ Weight
- ❑ Runway Conditions

THE PILOT'S OPERATING HANDBOOK

- ❑ Performance Charts
- ❑ Takeoff Charts
- ❑ Climb Performance Charts
- ❑ Cruise Performance Charts
- ❑ Descent Charts
- ❑ Landing Distance Charts
- ❑ Glide Distance
- ❑ Stall Speeds

COMPLETION STANDARDS:

- Demonstrate ability to understand and calculate aircraft performance data during oral quizzing by instructor at completion of lesson.
- Student completes Chapter 11 questions for Section B with a minimum passing score of 80%, and the instructor reviews incorrect responses to ensure complete understanding before the student to progresses to Ground Lesson 39.

STUDY ASSIGNMENT:

INSTRUMENT/COMMERCIAL

Chapter 12, Section C — Controlling Weight and Balance

STAGE V
GROUND LESSON 39

LESSON REFERENCES:

INSTRUMENT/COMMERCIAL

Chapter 12, Section C — Controlling Weight and Balance

RECOMMENDED SEQUENCE:

1. Lesson Introduction
2. Class Discussion

LESSON OBJECTIVES:

- Understand the importance of controlling weight and balance and its effects on aircraft performance.
- Learn the methods of computing weight and balance.

ACADEMIC CONTENT:

SECTION C — CONTROLLING WEIGHT AND BALANCE

- ❏ Weight and Balance Limitations
- ❏ Center of Gravity Limits
- ❏ Weight and Balance Documents
- ❏ Weight and Balance Computations
- ❏ Weight and Balance Condition Checks
- ❏ Computation Method
- ❏ Graph Method
- ❏ Table Method
- ❏ Weight Shift Computations

COMPLETION STANDARDS:

- Demonstrate understanding of aircraft weight and balance computations and performance effects during oral quizzing by instructor at completion of lesson.
- Student completes Chapter 12 questions for Section C with a minimum passing score of 80%, and the instructor reviews each incorrect response to ensure complete understanding before the student progresses to Ground Lesson 40.

STUDY ASSIGNMENT:

INSTRUMENT/COMMERCIAL

Chapter 14, Section A — Maximum Performance Takeoffs and Landings

STAGE V
GROUND LESSON 40

LESSON REFERENCES:

INSTRUMENT/COMMERCIAL
Chapter 14, Section A — Maximum Performance Takeoffs and Landings

GFD I/C VIDEO
Part IV, Chapter 14, Section A

RECOMMENDED SEQUENCE:

1. Lesson Introduction and Video Presentation
2. Class Discussion

LESSON OBJECTIVES:

- Understand the procedures and performance considerations necessary to execute maximum performance takeoffs and landings.

ACADEMIC CONTENT:

SECTION A — MAXIMUM PERFORMANCE TAKEOFFS AND LANDINGS

SOFT FIELD

- ❏ Takeoff and Climb
- ❏ Description/Procedure
- ❏ Approach and Landing

SHORT FIELD

- ❏ Takeoff and Maximum Performance Climb
- ❏ Description/Procedure
- ❏ Approach and Landing
- ❏ Combined Procedures

COMPLETION STANDARDS:

- Demonstrate understanding of maximum performance takeoffs and landings during oral quizzing by instructor at completion of lesson.
- Student completes Chapter 14 questions for Section A with a minimum passing score of 80%, and the instructor reviews each incorrect response to ensure complete understanding before the student progresses to Ground Lesson 41.

STUDY ASSIGNMENT:

INSTRUMENT/COMMERCIAL
Chapter 14, Section B — Steep Turns and Section C — Chandelles

---

STAGE V
GROUND LESSON 41

LESSON REFERENCES:

INSTRUMENT/COMMERCIAL
Chapter 14, Section B — Steep Turns and Section C — Chandelles

GFD I/C VIDEO
Part IV, Chapter 14, Sections B and C

RECOMMENDED SEQUENCE:

1. Lesson Introduction and Video Presentation
2. Class Discussion

LESSON OBJECTIVES:

- Introduce steep turns and chandelles including performance factors and safety considerations relevant to the maneuvers.

ACADEMIC CONTENT:

SECTION B — STEEP TURNS

- ❏ Steep Turns
- ❏ Description/Procedure

SECTION C — CHANDELLES

- ❏ Chandelles
- ❏ Description/Procedure

COMPLETION STANDARDS:

- Demonstrate understanding of steep turns and chandelles during oral quizzing by instructor at completion of lesson.

- Student completes Chapter 14 questions for Sections B and C with a minimum passing score of 80%, and the instructor reviews each incorrect response to ensure complete understanding before the student progresses to Ground Lesson 42.

STUDY ASSIGNMENT:

INSTRUMENT/COMMERCIAL

Chapter 14, Section D — Lazy Eights, Section E — Eights-on-Pylons, Section F — Steep Spirals, and Section G — Power-Off 180° Accuracy Approach and Landing

---

STAGE V
GROUND LESSON 42

LESSON REFERENCES:

INSTRUMENT/COMMERCIAL

Chapter 14, Section D — Lazy Eights, Section E — Eights-on-Pylons, Section F — Steep Spirals, and Section G — Power-Off 180° Accuracy Approach and Landing

GFD I/C VIDEO

Part IV, Chapter 14, Sections D, E, F, and G

RECOMMENDED SEQUENCE:

1. Lesson Introduction and Video Presentation
2. Class Discussion

LESSON OBJECTIVES:

- Learn how to fly lazy eights, eights-on-pylons, and steep spiral maneuvers.
- Acquire knowledge of how maneuvers introduced during the commercial pilot phase of training develop pilot skill.

ACADEMIC CONTENT:

SECTION D — LAZY EIGHTS

❑ Lazy Eights
❑ Description/Procedure

SECTION E — EIGHTS-ON-PYLONS

❑ Eights-On-Pylons
❑ Description/Procedure

SECTION F — STEEP SPIRALS

❑ Steep Spirals
❑ Description/Procedure

SECTION G — POWER-OFF 180° ACCURACY APPROACH AND LANDING

❑ Power-Off 180° Accuracy Approach and Landing
❑ Description/Procedure

COMPLETION STANDARDS:

- Demonstrate understanding of lazy eights, eights-on-pylons, steep spirals, and power-off 180° accuracy approaches and landings during oral quizzing by instructor at completion of lesson.
- Student completes Chapter 14 questions for Sections D, E, F, and G with a minimum passing score of 80%, and the instructor reviews each incorrect response to ensure complete understanding before the student progresses to Ground Lesson 43.

STUDY ASSIGNMENT:

INSTRUMENT/COMMERCIAL

Chapter 13, Section A — Emergency Procedures

STAGE V GROUND LESSON 43

LESSON REFERENCES:

INSTRUMENT/COMMERCIAL

Chapter 13, Section A — Emergency Procedures

RECOMMENDED SEQUENCE:

1. Lesson Introduction
2. Class Discussion

LESSON OBJECTIVES:

- Understand the emergency procedures for various situations during commercial flight operations under VFR.
- Become familiar with some basic forced landing procedures, emergency equipment, and survival gear.

ACADEMIC CONTENT:

SECTION A — EMERGENCY PROCEDURES

❏ Emergency Descent
❏ Emergency Approach and Landing
❏ In-Flight Fire
❏ Partial Power Loss
❏ Door Opening in Flight
❏ Asymmetrical Flap Extension
❏ Emergency Equipment and Survival Gear

COMPLETION STANDARDS:

- Demonstrate understanding of commercial pilot emergency procedures during oral quizzing by instructor at completion of lesson.
- Student completes Chapter 13 questions for Section A with a minimum passing score of 80%, and the instructor reviews each incorrect response to ensure complete understanding before the student progresses to Ground Lesson 44.

STUDY ASSIGNMENT:

INSTRUMENT/COMMERCIAL

Chapter 13, Section B — Commercial Decision Making

STAGE V

GROUND LESSON 44

LESSON REFERENCES:

INSTRUMENT/COMMERCIAL

Chapter 13, Section B — Commercial Decision Making

RECOMMENDED SEQUENCE:

1. Lesson Introduction
2. Class Discussion

LESSON OBJECTIVES:

- Understand the decision-making process related to commercial flight operations.
- Learn how human factors affect aeronautical decision making and how crew resource management skills can enhance flight safety.

ACADEMIC CONTENT:

SECTION B — COMMERCIAL DECISION MAKING

- ❑ Commercial Operations
- ❑ Applying the Decision-Making Process
- ❑ Crew Resource Management
- ❑ Hazardous Attitudes
- ❑ Crew Relationships
- ❑ Communication
- ❑ Barriers to Effective Communication
- ❑ Resource Use
- ❑ Internal and External Resources
- ❑ Workload Management
- ❑ Planning and Preparation
- ❑ Prioritizing
- ❑ Situational Awareness
- ❑ Controlled Flight Into Terrain

COMPLETION STANDARDS:

- Demonstrate thorough understanding of the commercial decision making during oral quizzing by instructor at completion of lesson.
- Student completes Chapter 13 questions for Section B with a minimum passing score of 80%, and the instructor reviews each incorrect response to ensure complete understanding before the student progresses to the Stage V Exam in Ground Lesson 45.

STUDY ASSIGNMENT:

Review Chapters 11 – 14 in preparation for the Stage V Exam.

STAGE V

GROUND LESSON 45

STAGE V EXAM

LESSON REFERENCES:

INSTRUMENT/COMMERCIAL

Chapters 11, 12, 13, and 14

RECOMMENDED SEQUENCE:

1. Lesson Introduction
2. Testing
3. Critique

LESSON OBJECTIVES:

- Administer the stage exam covering knowledge of advanced airplane systems and performance, aeronautical decision making and other material covered in Chapters 11, 12, 13, and 14 of the *Instrument/Commercial* textbook.

ACADEMIC CONTENT:

STAGE V EXAM

- ❑ High Performance Powerplants
- ❑ Environmental and Ice Control Systems
- ❑ Retractable Landing Gear
- ❑ Advanced Aerodynamics
- ❑ Predicting Airplane Performance
- ❑ Controlling Weight and Balance
- ❑ Commercial Flight Maneuvers
- ❑ Emergency Procedures
- ❑ Commercial Decision Making

COMPLETION STANDARDS:

- The lesson and stage are complete when the student has passed the Stage V Exam with a minimum passing of 80%, and the instructor has reviewed each incorrect response to ensure complete understanding before the student progresses to the Commercial Pilot End-of-Course Exam.

STUDY ASSIGNMENT:

INSTRUMENT/COMMERCIAL

Review Chapters 11 – 14 in preparation for the Commercial Pilot End-of-Course Exam.

STAGE V
GROUND LESSON 46
END-OF-COURSE EXAM

LESSON REFERENCES:

INSTRUMENT/COMMERCIAL

Chapters 11, 12, 13, and 14

GUIDED FLIGHT DISCOVERY TRAINING VIDEOS

RECOMMENDED SEQUENCE:

1. Lesson Introduction
2. Testing
3. Critique

LESSON OBJECTIVES:

- Demonstrate comprehension of academic material presented in preparation for the FAA commercial pilot airmen knowledge test.

ACADEMIC CONTENT:

❑ The student will complete a comprehensive exam to include all knowledge areas found in the FAA commercial pilot airmen knowledge test.

COMPLETION STANDARDS:

- The lesson and the ground training portion of the commercial course are complete when the student has passed the Commercial Pilot End-of-Course Exam with a minimum score of 80%, and the instructor has reviewed each incorrect response to ensure complete understanding before the student progresses to the commercial pilot airmen knowledge test.

STUDY ASSIGNMENT:

Review *Instrument/Commercial* textbook Chapters 11 — 14, as well as the additional material, if required, in preparation for the FAA commercial pilot airmen knowledge test.

COMMERCIAL PILOT CERTIFICATION STAGE IV

STAGE OBJECTIVES

The objective of Stage IV is to broaden the student's knowledge of VFR cross-country and night operations and provide the skill necessary to operate safely in the night environment and during extended cross-country flights.

STAGE COMPLETION STANDARDS

This stage is complete when the student can demonstrate the complete and accurate planning of VFR cross-country flights and safe conduct of those flights using pilotage, dead reckoning, and navigation systems. In addition, the student must demonstrate safe night flight operations.

STAGE IV FLIGHT LESSON 30

DUAL — CROSS-COUNTRY

RECOMMENDED SEQUENCE:

1. Preflight Orientation: Briefing — Cross-Country Procedures
2. Flight
3. Postflight Evaluation

LESSON OBJECTIVES:

- The student will review VFR cross-country skills including the demonstration of simulated emergency procedures in preparation for solo cross-country flights.
- The flight will be at least two hours in duration and include a straight-line distance of more than 100 nautical miles from the original departure point.

REVIEW:

PREFLIGHT PREPARATION

- ❑ Cross-Country Flight Planning
- ❑ Airworthiness Requirements
- ❑ Certificates and Documents
- ❑ Performance and Limitations
- ❑ National Airspace System
- ❑ Weather Information
- ❑ Cockpit Management
- ❑ Crew Resource Management
- ❑ Density Altitude Considerations
- ❑ Engine Starting, Taxiing, Before Takeoff Check
- ❑ High Density Altitude Operations

INFLIGHT OPERATIONS

- ❑ Radio Communications and ATC Light Signals
- ❑ Navigation Systems and Radar Services
- ❑ Pilotage and Dead Reckoning
- ❑ Diversion and Lost Procedures
- ❑ Power Settings
- ❑ Mixture Leaning
- ❑ Radio Facility Shutdown

SIMULATED EMERGENCY PROCEDURES

- ❑ Systems and Equipment Malfunctions
- ❑ Low Fuel Supply
- ❑ Adverse Weather
- ❑ Airframe and Powerplant Icing
- ❑ Emergency Approach and Landing (Simulated)
- ❑ Wake Turbulence Avoidance
- ❑ Emergency Equipment and Survival Gear

UNFAMILIAR AIRPORTS

- ❑ Traffic Patterns
- ❑ Non-towered Airport
- ❑ UNICOM-Equipped Airport
- ❑ Tower-Controlled Airport
- ❑ Operations in Heavy Traffic
- ❑ Operations at Sod or Unimproved Field

- ❑ CTAF Procedures
- ❑ Airport, Runway, and Taxiway Signs, Markings, and Lighting

FULL PANEL INSTRUMENT

- ❑ Straight-and-Level Flight
- ❑ Climbs
- ❑ Descents
- ❑ Standard-Rate Turns
- ❑ VOR Navigation
- ❑ NDB Navigation
- ❑ Use of Radar Vectors

COMPLETION STANDARDS:

- The student will demonstrate the ability to act as pilot in command on a cross-country flight of at least two hours to include a straight-line distance of more than 100 nautical miles from the original departure point.

NOTE: *The instrument portion of this lesson should be accomplished on an as required basis depending on an assessment of the student's capabilities. Students enrolled in the Commercial Pilot Certification Course only must complete 5 hours of instrument training to meet the requirements of FAR Part 141, Appendix D.*

POSTFLIGHT DISCUSSION AND PREVIEW OF NEXT LESSON

STUDY ASSIGNMENT:

GROUND LESSON 30 —
Aviation Physiology

STAGE IV
FLIGHT LESSON 31

DUAL — LOCAL

NIGHT

RECOMMENDED SEQUENCE:

1. Preflight Orientation
2. Flight
3. Postflight Evaluation

LESSON OBJECTIVES:

- The student will be introduced to night flying operations and the special precautions required for flight at night.
- Review emergency procedures appropriate to night operations.

REVIEW:

- ❑ Normal Takeoffs and Climbs
- ❑ Normal Approaches and Landings
- ❑ Go-Around/Rejected Landing
- ❑ Steep Turns
- ❑ Unusual Attitudes
- ❑ Maneuvering During Slow Flight
- ❑ Simulated Emergency Procedures

INTRODUCE:

- ❑ Night Preflight Preparation
- ❑ Aircraft Lighting and Equipment
- ❑ Aeromedical Factors
- ❑ Physiological Aspects of Night Flight
- ❑ Personal Equipment Recommended
- ❑ Engine Starting, Taxiing, Before Takeoff Check
- ❑ Night VFR References
- ❑ Lost Procedures
- ❑ Night Scanning/Collision Avoidance

COMPLETION STANDARDS:

- The student will demonstrate knowledge of and the precautions and the procedures appropriate to flying at night.
- The student will be evaluated based on the exercise of sound judgment and on his/her ability to command the aircraft during the flight.

POSTFLIGHT DISCUSSION AND PREVIEW OF NEXT LESSON

STUDY ASSIGNMENT:

GROUND LESSON 31 —
Aeronautical Decision Making

STAGE IV FLIGHT LESSON 32

DUAL — CROSS-COUNTRY, NIGHT

RECOMMENDED SEQUENCE:

1. Preflight Orientation
2. Flight
3. Postflight Evaluation

LESSON OBJECTIVES:

- During this lesson, the student will learn night cross-country procedures, including preflight planning, navigation, emergencies, and the use of unfamiliar airports.
- The flight will be at least two hours in duration and include a straight-line distance of more than 100 nautical miles from the original departure point.

REVIEW:

- ❑ Aeromedical Factors and Physiological Aspects
- ❑ Aircraft Lighting and Equipment
- ❑ Airworthiness Requirements
- ❑ Engine Starting, Taxiing, Before Takeoff Check
- ❑ Normal Takeoffs and Landings
- ❑ Go-Around/Rejected Landing
- ❑ Unfamiliar Airports

SIMULATED EMERGENCY PROCEDURES

- ❑ Systems and Equipment Malfunctions
- ❑ Adverse Weather
- ❑ Wake Turbulence Avoidance
- ❑ Low Fuel Supply
- ❑ Airframe and Powerplant Icing

FULL PANEL INSTRUMENT

- ❑ Straight-and-Level Flight
- ❑ Climbs and Descents
- ❑ Standard-Rate Turns

INTRODUCTION:

NIGHT PREFLIGHT PREPARATION

- ❑ Cross-Country Flight Planning
- ❑ Weather Information
- ❑ Preflight Inspection
- ❑ Cockpit Management
- ❑ Crew Resource Management
- ❑ Airport, Runway, and Taxiway Signs, Markings, and Lighting
- ❑ Runway Incursion Avoidance
- ❑ Land and Hold Short Operations (LAHSO)

NIGHT NAVIGATION

- ❑ Night Cross-Country Procedures
- ❑ Navigation Systems and Radar Services
- ❑ Pilotage and Dead Reckoning
- ❑ Diversion and Lost Procedures

COMPLETION STANDARDS:

- Successful completion of this lesson is indicated by the student's demonstration of the correct operating procedures for night cross-country flights.
- The flight will be at least two hours in duration and include a straight-line distance of more than 100 nautical miles from the original departure point.

NOTE: *The instrument portion of this lesson should be accomplished on an as required basis depending on an assessment of the student's capabilities. Students enrolled in the Commercial Pilot Certification Course only must complete 5 hours of instrument training to meet the requirements of FAR Part 141, Appendix D.*

POSTFLIGHT DISCUSSION AND PREVIEW OF NEXT LESSON

STUDY ASSIGNMENT:

GROUND LESSON 32 —
Commercial FARs

STAGE IV FLIGHT LESSONS 33 AND 34

SOLO — LOCAL NIGHT

RECOMMENDED SEQUENCE:

1. Preflight Orientation
2. Flight
3. Postflight Evaluation

LESSON OBJECTIVES:

- These lessons provide night solo practice so the student may gain proficiency and confidence in the night environment.

REVIEW:

- ❑ Maneuvering During Slow Flight
- ❑ Constant Altitude Turns
- ❑ Takeoffs and Landings (Normal and/or Crosswind)

NOTE: *The 10 night takeoffs and landings with each involving flight in the traffic pattern at an airport with an operating control tower are an FAR Part 141 requirement. Five should be completed in Flight Lesson 33 and the other five in Flight Lesson 34. However, this requirement may be accomplished with fewer than five per flight, as long as the total of 10 is completed.*

COMPLETION STANDARDS:

- Lessons 33 and 34 are complete when the student has conducted both solo night flights. During the Flights, the student should attempt to gain proficiency in takeoffs and landings at an airport with an operating control tower in the night environment.

POSTFLIGHT DISCUSSION AND PREVIEW OF NEXT LESSON

STAGE IV FLIGHT LESSON 35

SOLO — CROSS-COUNTRY, NIGHT

RECOMMENDED SEQUENCE:

1. Preflight Orientation
2. Flight
3. Postflight Evaluation

LESSON OBJECTIVES:

- The student's proficiency in night operations is reviewed and practiced in this lesson.
- During this lesson, the student should acquire increased knowledge of radio navigation during cross-country flights. The flight will include a landing at a point more than 50 nautical miles from the original departure point.

REVIEW:

CROSS-COUNTRY FLIGHT ASSIGNED BY THE INSTRUCTOR

- ❑ Cross-Country Flight Planning
- ❑ Weather Information
- ❑ Night Operation Considerations
- ❑ Preflight Preparations
- ❑ Cockpit Management

NIGHT NAVIGATION

- ❑ Night Cross-Country Procedures
- ❑ Navigation Systems and Radar Services
- ❑ Pilotage and Dead Reckoning
- ❑ Crew Resource Management
- ❑ Airport, Runway, and Taxiway Signs, Markings, and Lighting
- ❑ Runway Incursion Avoidance

COMPLETION STANDARDS:

- The student will show added skill in cross-country planning by selecting optimum cruising altitudes and appropriate checkpoints for a flight with a landing at a point more than 50 nautical miles from the original departure point.
- Demonstrate ability to accomplish the assigned night cross-country flight.
- During the postflight evaluation, the student will thoroughly explain the operational and safety considerations associated with night cross-country flying.

POSTFLIGHT DISCUSSION AND PREVIEW OF NEXT LESSON

STUDY ASSIGNMENT:

GROUND LESSON 33 —
Prepare, as necessary, for the Stage IV Exam.

NOTE: *The night solo training time requirements for this lesson may be completed in more than one flight.*

STAGE IV FLIGHT LESSON 36

SOLO (DUAL) — CROSS-COUNTRY

LESSON OBJECTIVES:

- This and the following flights are provided to develop the student's cross-country proficiency and confidence.
- These lessons may also be utilized for additional dual instruction necessary to meet the proficiency requirements for the end-of-course flight check and FAA practical test.

REVIEW:

- ❏ Preflight Preparation
- ❏ Cross-Country Flight Planning
- ❏ Cross-Country Flight Assigned by the Instructor
- ❏ Cockpit Management
- ❏ Crew Resource Management
- ❏ Dead Reckoning
- ❏ Pilotage
- ❏ VOR Navigation

COMPLETION STANDARDS:

- The student will show added skill in cross-country planning by selecting optimum cruising altitudes and appropriate checkpoints for a flight with a landing at a point more than 50 nautical miles from the original departure point.
- Demonstrate fuel planning by accurately calculating fuel burn and provisions for an adequate reserve upon landing. If the lesson is used for dual instruction, the student should demonstrate increased proficiency in the listed areas of operation and tasks.

POSTFLIGHT DISCUSSION AND PREVIEW OF NEXT LESSON

STAGE IV FLIGHT LESSON 37

SOLO (DUAL) — CROSS-COUNTRY

LESSON OBJECTIVES:

- This lesson develops student proficiency in cross-country flights in an unfamiliar area. The flight will include a landing at a point more than 50 nautical miles from the original departure point. This lesson may also be utilized for additional dual instruction to meet the proficiency requirements for the end-of-course flight check and FAA practical test.

REVIEW:

CROSS-COUNTRY FLIGHT ASSIGNED BY THE INSTRUCTOR

- ❏ Preflight Preparation
- ❏ Use of Tower-Controlled Airport
- ❏ Use of UNICOM-Equipped Airport

COMPLETION STANDARDS:

- This lesson is complete when the student has conducted a solo cross-country to include a landing at a point more than 50 nautical miles from the original departure point. The student should attempt to gain proficiency in cross-country operations and the use of unfamiliar airports. If the lesson is used for dual instruction, the student should demonstrate increased proficiency in the tasks or areas of operation reviewed.

STAGE IV
FLIGHT LESSON 38
SOLO (DUAL) —
CROSS-COUNTRY

LESSON OBJECTIVES:

- The objective of this lesson is for the student to plan and complete a cross-country flight using pilotage, dead reckoning, and radio navigation. The flight will include a landing at a point more than 50 nautical miles from the original departure point. This lesson may also be utilized for additional dual instruction, to meet the proficiency requirements for the end-of-course flight check and FAA practical test.

REVIEW:

CROSS-COUNTRY FLIGHT ASSIGNED BY THE INSTRUCTOR

❑ Preflight Preparation
❑ Cross-Country Flight Planning
❑ Pilotage
❑ Dead Reckoning
❑ VOR Navigation
❑ NDB Navigation

COMPLETION STANDARDS

- This lesson is complete when the student has conducted a solo cross-country to include a landing at a point more than 50 nautical miles from the original departure point.
- The student should attempt to gain proficiency in the accurate tracking of selected VOR radials and NDB bearings. If the lesson is used for dual instruction the student should demonstrate increased proficiency in the tasks or areas of operation reviewed.

POSTFLIGHT DISCUSSION AND PREVIEW OF NEXT LESSON

STAGE IV
FLIGHT LESSON 39
SOLO (DUAL) —
CROSS-COUNTRY

LESSON OBJECTIVES:

- This lesson provides increased proficiency and broadens the student's cross-country experience. The flight will include a landing at a point more than 50 nautical miles from the original departure point. This lesson may also be utilized for additional dual instruction to meet the proficiency requirements for the end-of-course flight check and FAA practical test.

REVIEW:

CROSS-COUNTRY FLIGHT ASSIGNED BY THE INSTRUCTOR

❑ Preflight Preparation
❑ Cross-Country Flight Planning
❑ Pilotage
❑ VOR Navigation
❑ Use of Non-towered Airport

COMPLETION STANDARDS:

- This lesson is complete when the student has conducted a solo cross-country to include a landing at a point more than 50 nautical miles from the original departure point. If the lesson is used for dual instruction, the student should demonstrate increased proficiency in the tasks or areas of operation reviewed.

POSTFLIGHT DISCUSSION AND PREVIEW OF NEXT LESSON

STAGE IV FLIGHT LESSON 40

SOLO (DUAL) — CROSS-COUNTRY

LESSON OBJECTIVES:

- During this lesson, the student should acquire increased knowledge of radio navigation during cross-country flights. The flight will include a landing at a point more than 50 nautical miles from the original departure point. This lesson may also be utilized for additional dual instruction to meet the proficiency requirements for the end-of-course flight check and FAA practical test.

REVIEW:

CROSS-COUNTRY FLIGHT ASSIGNED BY THE INSTRUCTOR

- ❑ Preflight Preparation
- ❑ Cross-Country Flight Planning
- ❑ VOR Navigation
- ❑ NDB Navigation
- ❑ Use of Tower-Controlled Airport
- ❑ Use of Non-towered Airport

COMPLETION STANDARDS:

- The student should realize increased confidence and proficiency in the use of radio aids and navigation techniques over unfamiliar terrain in a flight which includes a landing at a point more than 50 nautical miles from the original departure point. If the lesson is used for dual instruction, the student should demonstrate increased proficiency in the tasks or areas of operation reviewed.

POSTFLIGHT DISCUSSION AND PREVIEW OF NEXT LESSON

STAGE IV FLIGHT LESSON 41

SOLO (DUAL) — CROSS-COUNTRY

LESSON OBJECTIVES:

- This cross-country flight is used to build the student's skills in the use of pilotage and dead reckoning navigation. The flight will include a landing at a point more than 50 nautical miles from the original departure point. This lesson may also be utilized for additional dual instruction to meet the proficiency requirements for the end-of-course flight check and FAA practical test.

REVIEW:

CROSS-COUNTRY FLIGHT ASSIGNED BY THE INSTRUCTOR

- ❑ Preflight Preparation
- ❑ Cross-Country Flight Planning
- ❑ Pilotage
- ❑ Dead Reckoning

COMPLETION STANDARDS:

- This lesson is complete when the student has conducted a solo cross-country to include a landing at a point more than 50 nautical miles from the original departure point.
- The student's level of proficiency will be determined by comparing the revised ETA to the ATA at each checkpoint. The difference should not be greater than ±5 minutes. The estimate for the destination should be ±10 minutes. If the lesson is used for dual instruction, the student should demonstrate increased proficiency in the tasks or areas of operation reviewed.

POSTFLIGHT DISCUSSION AND PREVIEW OF NEXT LESSON

Stage IV Flight Lesson 42

Dual — Cross-Country

Lesson Objectives:

- During this lesson, the student will continue to practice cross-country planning and accurate flying. The flight will include a landing at a point more than 50 nautical miles from the original departure point.

Review:

Cross-Country Flight Assigned by the Instructor

- ❑ Preflight Preparation
- ❑ Cross-Country Flight Planning
- ❑ VOR Navigation
- ❑ NDB Navigation
- ❑ Use of Towered or Non-towered Airports

Completion Standards:

- This lesson is complete when the student has conducted a cross-country to include a landing at a point more than 50 nautical miles from the original departure point demonstrating increased proficiency by accurately adhering to the preplanned navigation log.

Postflight Discussion and Preview of Next Lesson

Stage IV Flight Lesson 43

Solo — Cross-Country

Recommended Sequence:

1. Preflight Orientation
2. Flight
3. Postflight Evaluation

Lesson Objectives:

- The purpose of this cross country is to build the student's experience and meet the long cross-country requirements. Therefore, the flight must include landings at a minimum of three points, one of which is at least 250 nautical miles straight line distance from the original departure point. If the flight is conducted in Hawaii, the alternate provisions of FAR 141, Appendix D, apply.

Review:

Cross-Country Flight Assigned by the Instructor

- ❑ Preflight Preparation
- ❑ Cross-Country Flight Planning
- ❑ Cockpit Management
- ❑ Pilotage
- ❑ Dead Reckoning
- ❑ VOR Navigation
- ❑ NDB Navigation
- ❑ Use of Tower-Controlled Airport
- ❑ Use of Non-towered Airport

Completion Standards:

- This lesson is complete when the student has conducted a solo cross-country with landings at a minimum of three points, one of which is at least 250 nautical miles straight line distance from the original departure point.
- During the preflight orientation and postflight evaluation, the student should be able to flight plan accurately making use of the applicable FAA publications and weather analysis information.

Postflight Discussion and Preview of Next Lesson

STAGE IV FLIGHT LESSON 44

DUAL — CROSS-COUNTRY

STAGE IV CHECK

RECOMMENDED SEQUENCE:

1. Preflight Orientation
2. Flight
3. Postflight Evaluation

LESSON OBJECTIVES:

- The objective of this stage check, conducted by the chief instructor, the assistant chief, or a designated check instructor, is to evaluate the student's understanding of VFR cross-country procedures and to determine the student's ability to perform these procedures at the proficiency level of a commercial pilot.

REVIEW:

CROSS-COUNTRY FLIGHT

❏ Preflight Preparation
❏ National Airspace System
❏ Cross-Country Flight Planning
❏ Cockpit Management
❏ Crew Resource Management
❏ VOR Navigation
❏ Pilotage
❏ Dead Reckoning
❏ Cruise Procedures
❏ Use of Unfamiliar Airports
❏ Airport, Runway, and Taxiway Signs, Markings, and Lighting
❏ Radio Communications and ATC Light Signals
❏ Runway Incursion Avoidance

SIMULATED EMERGENCY PROCEDURES

❏ Systems and Equipment Malfunctions
❏ Low Fuel Supply
❏ Lost Procedures
❏ Turbulence
❏ Adverse Weather
❏ Airframe and Powerplant Icing
❏ Diversion
❏ Radio and Instrument Failure
❏ Radio Facility Shutdown
❏ High Density Altitude Operations

COMPLETION STANDARDS:

- At the completion of this lesson, the student will display a complete understanding of VFR cross-country planning and flight procedures. The student will show the ability to operate safely in the national airspace system and use good judgment consistently.

POSTFLIGHT DISCUSSION AND PREVIEW OF EXT LESSON

STAGE V

STAGE OBJECTIVES

Stage V is to provide instruction and practice in the complex aircraft. The stage objective is to broaden the student's knowledge and provide the skill necessary to safely fly a complex airplane which is similar to those frequently used in commercial operations. Additionally, the introduction and practice of commercial maneuvers is included so the student can begin acquiring proficiency.

STAGE COMPLETION STANDARDS

This stage is complete when the student can demonstrate commercial pilot proficiency in the operation of the complex aircraft and basic knowledge of the advanced commercial maneuvers.

STAGE V FLIGHT LESSON 45

SOLO — LOCAL

LESSON OBJECTIVES:

- Provide the student with the opportunity to practice basic flight maneuvers to further develop coordination and airplane control in preparation for introduction to the complex aircraft.

REVIEW:

- ❑ Power-Off Stalls
- ❑ Power-On Stalls
- ❑ Maneuvering During Slow Flight
- ❑ Normal Takeoffs and Landings
- ❑ Private Pilot Ground Reference Maneuvers Assigned by the Instructor

COMPLETION STANDARDS:

- This lesson is complete when the student has conducted the assigned flight. The student should attempt to gain proficiency in the planning and performance of each maneuver.

POSTFLIGHT DISCUSSION AND PREVIEW OF NEXT LESSON

STUDY ASSIGNMENT:

GROUND LESSONS 34, 35, AND 36 —
High Performance Powerplants, Environmental and Ice Control Systems, and Retractable Landing Gear.
Prepare for the Complex Aircraft Transition Briefing for Flight Lesson 46.

STAGE V
FLIGHT LESSON 46

DUAL — LOCAL

COMPLEX AIRCRAFT

RECOMMENDED SEQUENCE:

1. Preflight Orientation: Briefing — Complex Aircraft Transition
2. Flight
3. Postflight Evaluation

LESSON OBJECTIVES:

- The objective of Flight Lesson 46 is to introduce the student to the complex airplane including systems and basic flight operations.
- The use of high altitude systems will be introduced, if applicable to the airplane to be used for the practical test.

INTRODUCE:

PREFLIGHT PREPARATIONS AND GROUND OPERATIONS

❏ Certificates and Documents
❏ Airworthiness Requirements
❏ Operation of Systems
❏ Performance and Limitations
❏ Use of Checklists
❏ Cockpit Management
❏ Preflight Inspection
❏ Engine Starting and Taxiing
❏ Before Takeoff Check

TAKEOFFS AND LANDINGS

❏ Use of Retractable Landing Gear and Flaps
❏ Normal and Crosswind
❏ Climbs and Descents
❏ Go-Around/Rejected Landing

CRUISE PROCEDURES

❏ Power Settings and Mixture Leaning
❏ Use of Constant-Speed Propeller and Effects Upon Aircraft Performance

POSTFLIGHT PROCEDURES

❏ After Landing
❏ Parking
❏ Securing

HIGH ALTITUDE OPERATIONS

❏ Supplemental Oxygen
❏ Pressurization

COMPLETION STANDARDS:

- The student should display a working knowledge of the airplane systems.
- The student should will exhibit at least private pilot proficiency in the performance of basic flight operations.

NOTE: *If high altitude systems are not applicable to the airplane to be used for the practical test, the student must still demonstrate knowledge of high altitude operations sufficient to meet the requirements specified in the FAA Commercial Pilot Practical Test Standards.*

POSTFLIGHT DISCUSSION AND PREVIEW OF NEXT LESSON

STUDY ASSIGNMENT:

GROUND LESSON 37 —
Advanced Aerodynamics

STAGE V FLIGHT LESSONS 47 AND 48

DUAL — LOCAL

COMPLEX AIRCRAFT

RECOMMENDED SEQUENCE:

1. Preflight Orientation
2. Flight
3. Postflight Evaluation

LESSON OBJECTIVES:

- Review basic flight procedures.
- Introduce and practice emergency procedures, attitude instrument flying, and takeoffs and landings in the complex aircraft.
- Develop the necessary proficiency to safely act as pilot in command in the aircraft.

REVIEW:

- ❑ Use of Checklists
- ❑ Preflight Inspection
- ❑ Performance and Limitations
- ❑ Takeoffs and Landings
- ❑ Go-Around/Rejected Landing
- ❑ Power Settings and Mixture Leaning
- ❑ Use of Constant-Speed Propeller and Effects Upon Aircraft Performance
- ❑ Use of Landing Gear and Flaps
- ❑ Climbs and Descents
- ❑ Constant Altitude Turns
- ❑ Maneuvering During Slow Flight
- ❑ Power-Off Stalls
- ❑ Power-On Stalls
- ❑ Emergency Approach and Landing (Simulated)
- ❑ Systems and Equipment Malfunctions

INTRODUCE:

TAKEOFFS AND LANDINGS

- ❑ Short-Field/Maximum Performance Climb
- ❑ Soft-Field
- ❑ At Maximum Authorized Takeoff Weight
- ❑ Combined Procedures

SIMULATED EMERGENCY PROCEDURE

- ❑ Fire in Flight

FULL PANEL INSTRUMENT

- ❑ Straight-and-Level Flight
- ❑ Climbs and Climbing Turns
- ❑ Descents and Descending Turns
- ❑ Standard-Rate Turns
- ❑ Recovery From Unusual Flight Attitudes
- ❑ Maneuvering During Slow Flight

COMPLETION STANDARDS:

- At the completion of Flight Lesson 48, the student should be thoroughly familiar with the flight characteristics, systems, and emergency procedures associated with the complex airplane.
- The student will demonstrate pilot-in-command proficiency.

NOTE: *The instrument portion of this lesson should be accomplished on an as required basis depending on an assessment of the student's capabilities. Students enrolled in the Commercial Pilot Certification Course only must complete 5 hours of instrument training to meet the requirements of FAR 141, Appendix D.*

POSTFLIGHT DISCUSSION AND PREVIEW OF NEXT LESSON

STUDY ASSIGNMENT:

GROUND LESSONS 38 AND 39 — Predicting Performance and Controlling Weight and Balance

STAGE V FLIGHT LESSONS 49 AND 50

DUAL — LOCAL

COMPLEX AIRCRAFT

RECOMMENDED SEQUENCE:

1. Preflight Orientation
2. Flight
3. Postflight Evaluation

LESSON OBJECTIVES:

- The student will perform the pilot in command responsibilities to increase familiarity with the complex airplane prior to the stage check.

REVIEW:

- ❑ Preflight Inspection
- ❑ Cruise Procedures
- ❑ Power Settings and Mixture Leaning
- ❑ Climbs
- ❑ Descents
- ❑ Constant Altitude Turns
- ❑ Maneuvering During Slow Flight
- ❑ Power-Off Stalls
- ❑ Power-On Stalls
- ❑ Short-Field Takeoffs/Maximum Performance Climbs and Landings
- ❑ Soft-Field Takeoffs and Landings

COMPLETION STANDARDS:

- During each flight, the student should attempt to increase proficiency in the smooth and accurate performance of the listed flight maneuvers in the complex airplane.

POSTFLIGHT DISCUSSION AND PREVIEW OF NEXT LESSON

STUDY ASSIGNMENT:

GROUND LESSON 40 —
Maximum Performance Takeoffs and Landings
Prepare for the Commercial Flight Maneuvers Briefing for Flight Lesson 51.

STAGE V FLIGHT LESSON 51

DUAL — LOCAL

RECOMMENDED SEQUENCE:

1. Preflight Orientation: Briefing — Commercial Flight Maneuvers
2. Flight
3. Postflight Evaluation

LESSON OBJECTIVES:

- Review performance maneuvers and slow flight to further develop student skills in flying the airplane near its limits.
- Continue to practice performance landings and takeoffs.
- Additional practice with stalls and stall recovery during all phases of flight.

NOTE: *The demonstrated stalls are not a proficiency requirement for commercial pilot certification. The purpose of the demonstrations is to reinforce private pilot knowledge of these stalls and help the student recognize, prevent, and if necessary, recover before the stall develops into a spin. These stalls should be practiced with a qualified flight instructor. Some stalls may be prohibited in some airplanes.*

REVIEW:

- ❑ Flight at Slow Airspeeds
- ❑ Recognition of and Recovery from Stalls Entered from Straight Flight and from Turns
- ❑ Spin Awareness
- ❑ Collision Avoidance
- ❑ Short-Field Takeoffs/Maximum Performance Climbs and Landings
- ❑ Soft-Field Takeoffs and Landings

INTRODUCE:

DEMONSTRATED STALLS

- ❑ Secondary Stall
- ❑ Accelerated Maneuver Stall

- ❑ Crossed-Control Stall
- ❑ Elevator Trim Stall

COMPLETION STANDARDS:

- The student will display increased proficiency during steep turns by maintaining altitude ±150 feet and bank ±15°.
- The student will demonstrate the correct procedures for soft and short field landings by picking a point on the runway and landing not more than 100 feet beyond the selected point.
- The student will exhibit knowledge of stall and spin aerodynamics, including recognition and recovery procedures.

POSTFLIGHT DISCUSSION AND PREVIEW OF NEXT LESSON

STUDY ASSIGNMENT:

GROUND LESSON 41 —
Steep Turns and Chandelles

STAGE V
FLIGHT LESSON 52

DUAL — LOCAL

RECOMMENDED SEQUENCE:

1. Preflight Orientation
2. Flight
3. Postflight Evaluation

LESSON OBJECTIVES:

- This lesson provides a review of basic ground reference maneuvers.
- Steep turns and chandelles are introduced to begin developing precise airplane control when operating near the performance limits of the airplane.
- Additional practice in stall and spin recognition and recovery procedures will be provided.

NOTE: *The demonstrated stalls are not a proficiency requirement for commercial pilot certification. The purpose of the demonstrations is to reinforce private pilot knowledge of these stalls and help the student recognize, prevent, and if necessary, recover before the stall develops into a spin. These stalls should be practiced with a qualified flight instructor. Some stalls may be prohibited in some airplanes.*

REVIEW:

- ❑ Maneuvering During Slow Flight
- ❑ Flight at Slow Airspeeds
- ❑ Recognition of and Recovery from Stalls Entered from Straight Flight and from Turns
- ❑ Spin Awareness
- ❑ Simulated Emergency Procedures
- ❑ Emergency Approach and Landing (Simulated)
- ❑ Systems and Equipment Malfunctions

PRIVATE PILOT GROUND REFERENCE MANEUVERS ASSIGNED BY THE INSTRUCTOR

DEMONSTRATED STALLS

- ❑ Secondary Stall
- ❑ Accelerated Maneuver Stall
- ❑ Crossed-Control Stall
- ❑ Elevator Trim Stall

INTRODUCE:

- ❑ Steep Turns
- ❑ Chandelles

COMPLETION STANDARDS:

- The lesson is complete when the student can perform basic ground reference maneuvers while maintaining a specified altitude and ground track.
- The student will display an understanding of the entry, performance, and recovery from, steep turns and chandelles as well as display increased knowledge of stall and spin recognition and recovery.

POSTFLIGHT DISCUSSION AND PREVIEW OF NEXT LESSON

STUDY ASSIGNMENT:

GROUND LESSON 42 —
Lazy Eights, Eights-on-Pylons, and Steep Spirals

STAGE V FLIGHT LESSON 53

DUAL — LOCAL

RECOMMENDED SEQUENCE:

1. Preflight Orientation
2. Flight
3. Postflight Evaluation

LESSON OBJECTIVES:

- The student will develop a basic understanding of the hazards associated with low-level wind shear and wake turbulence.
- Lazy eights, eights-on-pylons, steep spirals, and power-off 180° accuracy approaches and landings are introduced to present the student with an added challenge in precision flight maneuvers.

REVIEW:

- ❑ Chandelles
- ❑ Normal Takeoffs and Landings
- ❑ Crosswind Takeoffs and Landings
- ❑ Low-Level Wind Shear

INTRODUCE:

- ❑ Lazy Eights
- ❑ Eights-On-Pylons
- ❑ Steep Spirals
- ❑ Wake Turbulence Avoidance
- ❑ Power-Off 180° Accuracy Approaches and Landings

COMPLETION STANDARDS:

- The student should show increased proficiency in the review maneuvers by demonstrating correct entry and recovery procedures and increased coordination during the performance of each maneuver.
- The student also will demonstrate an understanding of the hazards related to low-level wind shear and wake turbulence, as well as the important performance elements of lazy eights, eights-on-pylons, steep spirals, and power-off 180° accuracy approaches and landings.

POSTFLIGHT DISCUSSION AND PREVIEW OF NEXT LESSON

STAGE V FLIGHT LESSONS 54, 55, AND 56

SOLO — LOCAL

LESSON OBJECTIVES:

- The student will work to gain proficiency through review of the listed maneuvers.

REVIEW:

- ❑ Steep Turns
- ❑ Chandelles
- ❑ Lazy Eights
- ❑ Eights-on-Pylons
- ❑ Steep Spirals
- ❑ Maneuvering During Slow Flight
- ❑ Short-Field Takeoffs/Maximum Performance Climbs and Landings
- ❑ Soft-Field Takeoffs and Landings
- ❑ Power-Off 180° Accuracy Approaches and Landings
- ❑ Power-Off Stalls
- ❑ Power-On Stalls

COMPLETION STANDARDS:

- The three lessons are complete when the student has conducted the assigned flights. During the lessons, the student should attempt to minimize the transition and setup time between each maneuver.

POSTFLIGHT DISCUSSION AND PREVIEW OF NEXT LESSON

STAGE V FLIGHT LESSON 57

DUAL — LOCAL

RECOMMENDED SEQUENCE:

1. Preflight Orientation
2. Flight
3. Postflight Evaluation

LESSON OBJECTIVES:

- During this lesson the student is provided with a review of commercial maneuvers and attitude instrument flying.

REVIEW:

- ❑ Steep Turns
- ❑ Chandelles
- ❑ Lazy Eights
- ❑ Eights-On-Pylons
- ❑ Steep Spirals
- ❑ Power-On Stalls
- ❑ Power-Off Stalls

FULL AND PARTIAL PANEL INSTRUMENT

- ❑ Straight-and-Level Flight
- ❑ Standard-Rate Turns
- ❑ Power-Off Stalls
- ❑ Power-On Stalls
- ❑ Maneuvering During Slow Flight
- ❑ Recovery From Unusual Flight Attitudes

COMPLETION STANDARDS:

- The student will demonstrate increased proficiency in the listed commercial maneuvers and display competency in the instrument maneuvers according to the standards outlined in the current FAA Instrument Pilot Practical Test Standards.

NOTE: *The instrument portion of this lesson should be accomplished on an as required basis depending on an assessment of the student's capabilities. Students enrolled in the Commercial Pilot Certification Course only must complete 5 hours of instrument training to meet the requirements of FAR Part 141, Appendix D.*

POSTFLIGHT DISCUSSION AND PREVIEW OF NEXT LESSON

STUDY ASSIGNMENT:

GROUND LESSON 43 —
Emergency Procedures

STAGE V FLIGHT LESSON 58

DUAL — LOCAL

RECOMMENDED SEQUENCE:

1. Preflight Orientation
2. Flight
3. Postflight Evaluation

LESSON OBJECTIVES:

- During this lesson the student is provided with a review of commercial maneuvers, attitude instrument flying, and emergency operations.

REVIEW:

- ❑ Short Field Takeoffs and Maximum Performance Climbs
- ❑ Soft Field Takeoffs
- ❑ Short and Soft Field Landings
- ❑ Maneuvering During Slow Flight
- ❑ Power-On Stalls
- ❑ Power-Off Stalls
- ❑ Power-Off 180° Accuracy Approaches and Landings

FULL AND PARTIAL PANEL INSTRUMENT

- ❑ Straight-and-Level Flight
- ❑ Standard-Rate Turns
- ❑ Power-Off Stalls
- ❑ Power-On Stalls
- ❑ Maneuvering During Slow Flight

- ❑ Recovery From Unusual Flight Attitudes
- ❑ Emergency Operations

COMPLETION STANDARDS:

- The student will demonstrate increased proficiency in the listed commercial maneuvers and display competency in the instrument maneuvers and emergency operations according to the standards outlined in the current FAA Instrument Pilot Practical Test Standards.

NOTE: *The instrument portion of this lesson should be accomplished on an "as required" basis depending on an assessment of the student's capabilities. Students enrolled in the Commercial Pilot Certification Course must complete 5 hours of instrument training to meet the requirements of FAR Part 141, Appendix D.*

POSTFLIGHT DISCUSSION AND PREVIEW OF NEXT LESSON

STUDY ASSIGNMENT:

GROUND LESSON 44 —
Commercial Decision Making

STAGE V FLIGHT LESSONS 59, 60, AND 61

SOLO — LOCAL

LESSON OBJECTIVES:

- These lessons provide the student with the opportunity to review the listed flight maneuvers to increase proficiency.

REVIEW:

- ❑ Steep Turns
- ❑ Chandelles
- ❑ Lazy Eights
- ❑ Eights-On-Pylons
- ❑ Steep Spirals
- ❑ Short-Field Takeoffs/Maximum Performance Climbs and Landings
- ❑ Soft-Field Takeoffs and Landings
- ❑ Power-Off 180° Accuracy Approaches and Landings
- ❑ Aeronautical Decision Making and Judgment
- ❑ Cockpit Management

COMPLETION STANDARDS:

- These lessons are complete when the student has conducted the assigned solo flights developing additional proficiency in the listed maneuvers.

POSTFLIGHT DISCUSSION AND PREVIEW OF NEXT LESSON

STAGE V FLIGHT LESSONS 62 AND 63

SOLO — LOCAL

LESSON OBJECTIVES:

- The objective of flights 62 and 63 is to provide the student with the opportunity to review and practice flight maneuvers to gain added proficiency.

NOTE: *The instructor may decide to assign additional maneuvers and/or procedures on an as required basis.*

REVIEW:

- ❑ Power-Off Stalls
- ❑ Power-On Stalls
- ❑ Maneuvering During Slow Flight
- ❑ Steep Turns
- ❑ Chandelles
- ❑ Lazy Eights
- ❑ Eights-On-Pylons
- ❑ Steep Spirals
- ❑ Short-Field Takeoffs/Maximum Performance Climbs and Landings
- ❑ Soft-Field Takeoffs and Landings
- ❑ Power-Off 180° Accuracy Approaches and Landings

COMPLETION STANDARDS:

- The lessons are completed when the student has conducted the assigned maneuvers and/or procedures with increased accuracy and coordination.

POSTFLIGHT DISCUSSION AND PREVIEW OF NEXT LESSON

STAGE V FLIGHT LESSONS 64 AND 65

DUAL — LOCAL

RECOMMENDED SEQUENCE:

1. Preflight Orientation
2. Flight
3. Postflight Evaluation

LESSON OBJECTIVES:

- These lessons are designed to a review and evaluate the student's knowledge and proficiency in the operation of the tasks within the lesson. The flights provide an opportunity to practice the listed maneuvers and procedures in preparation for the stage check.

NOTE: *The instructor may decide to assign additional maneuvers and/or procedures on an as required basis.*

REVIEW:

- ❑ Power-Off Stalls
- ❑ Power-On Stalls
- ❑ Maneuvering During Slow Flight
- ❑ Steep Turns
- ❑ Chandelles
- ❑ Lazy Eights
- ❑ Eights-On-Pylons
- ❑ Steep Spirals
- ❑ Short-Field Takeoffs/Maximum Performance Climbs and Landings
- ❑ Soft-Field Takeoffs and Landings
- ❑ Power-Off 180° Accuracy Approaches and Landings

COMPLETION STANDARDS:

- These lessons are complete when the student demonstrates the ability to safely and accurately perform each of the assigned maneuvers and/or procedures. The student will demonstrate sufficient knowledge and proficiency to progress to Flight Lesson 66.

POSTFLIGHT DISCUSSION AND PREVIEW OF NEXT LESSON

STAGE V
FLIGHT LESSON 66
DUAL — LOCAL
COMPLEX AIRCRAFT

RECOMMENDED SEQUENCE:

1. Preflight Orientation
2. Flight
3. Postflight Evaluation

LESSON OBJECTIVES:

- This lesson is a review and evaluation of the student's knowledge and proficiency in the operation of the complex aircraft. The flight provides an opportunity to practice the listed maneuvers and procedures in preparation for the stage check.

NOTE: *The demonstrated stalls are not a proficiency requirement for commercial pilot certification. The purpose of the demonstrations in the complex airplane is to help the student reinforce private pilot knowledge of these stalls and how to recognize, prevent, and if necessary, recover before the stall develops into a spin. These stalls should be practiced with a qualified flight instructor. Some stalls may be prohibited in some airplanes.*

REVIEW:

- ❏ Preflight Preparation
- ❏ Airworthiness Requirements
- ❏ Preflight Inspection
- ❏ Cruise Procedures
- ❏ Power Settings and Mixture Leaning Climbs
- ❏ Descents
- ❏ Maneuvering During Slow Flight
- ❏ Power-Off Stalls
- ❏ Power-On Stalls
- ❏ Flight at Slow Airspeeds
- ❏ Recognition of and Recovery from Stalls Entered from Straight Flight and from Turns
- ❏ Spin Awareness
- ❏ Aeronautical Decision Making and Judgment
- ❏ Cockpit Management
- ❏ Postflight Procedures

TAKEOFFS AND LANDINGS

- ❏ Short-Field Takeoff and Maximum Performance Climb
- ❏ Soft-Field Takeoff and Climb
- ❏ Short-Field Approach and Landing
- ❏ Soft-Field Approach and Landing
- ❏ Power-Off 180° Accuracy Approach and Landing
- ❏ Go-Around/Rejected Landing

DEMONSTRATED STALLS

- ❏ Secondary Stall
- ❏ Accelerated Maneuver Stall
- ❏ Crossed-Control Stall
- ❏ Elevator Trim Stall

SIMULATED EMERGENCY PROCEDURES

- ❏ Systems and Equipment Malfunctions
- ❏ Low Fuel Supply
- ❏ Fire in Flight
- ❏ Turbulence
- ❏ Adverse Weather
- ❏ Airframe and Powerplant Icing
- ❏ Diversion
- ❏ Radio and Instrument Failure
- ❏ Landing Gear Malfunctions
- ❏ Emergency Approach and Landing (Simulated)
- ❏ Emergency Equipment and Survival Gear

COMPLETION STANDARDS:

- This lesson is complete when the student demonstrates the ability to safely act as pilot in command of the complex aircraft. The student will demonstrate sufficient knowledge and proficiency to pass the Stage V Check in Flight Lesson 67.

NOTE: *The instrument portion of this lesson should be accomplished on an as required basis depending on an assessment of the student's capabilities. Students enrolled in the Commercial Pilot Certification Course only must complete 5 hours of instrument training to meet the requirements of FAR Part 141, Appendix D.*

POSTFLIGHT DISCUSSION AND PREVIEW OF NEXT LESSON

STUDY ASSIGNMENT:

Prepare, as necessary, for the Stage V Exam in Ground Lesson 45 and the End-Of-Course Exam in Ground Lesson 46.

STAGE V
FLIGHT LESSON 67
DUAL — LOCAL
COMPLEX AIRCRAFT
STAGE V CHECK

RECOMMENDED SEQUENCE:
1. Preflight Orientation
2. Flight
3. Postflight Evaluation

LESSON OBJECTIVES:
- This stage check, conducted by the chief instructor, assistant chief instructor, or a designated check instructor, is provided to evaluate the student's pilot-in-command qualifications in the complex airplane.

REVIEW:
PREFLIGHT PREPARATIONS AND GROUND OPERATIONS
❑ Certificates and Documents
❑ Airworthiness Requirements
❑ Performance and Limitations
❑ Operation of Systems

FLIGHT OPERATIONS
❑ Preflight Inspection
❑ Cockpit Management
❑ Aeronautical Decision Making and Judgment
❑ Normal Takeoffs and Landings
❑ Crosswind Takeoffs and Landings
❑ Go-Around/Rejected Landing
❑ Power-Off Stalls
❑ Power-On Stalls
❑ Cruise Procedures
❑ Power Settings and Mixture Leaning
❑ Constant-Speed Propeller Effects on Aircraft Performance

FULL AND PARTIAL PANEL INSTRUMENT
❑ Straight-and-Level Flight
❑ Climbs
❑ Descents
❑ Turns
❑ Recovery From Unusual Flight Attitudes
❑ Power-On Stalls
❑ Power-Off Stalls

SIMULATED EMERGENCY PROCEDURES
❑ Systems and Equipment Malfunctions
❑ Landing Gear Malfunctions
❑ Fire in Flight

HIGH ALTITUDE OPERATIONS (AS REQUIRED)
❑ Supplemental Oxygen
❑ Pressurization

POSTFLIGHT PROCEDURES
❑ After Landing
❑ Parking
❑ Securing

COMPLETION STANDARDS:
- This lesson and Stage V are complete when the student can demonstrate commercial pilot proficiency, as outlined in the current FAA Commercial Pilot Practical Test Standards, in the operation of the complex airplane and the associated systems.

NOTE: *The instrument portion of this lesson should be accomplished on an as required basis depending on an assessment of the student's capabilities. Students enrolled in the Commercial Pilot Certification Course only must complete 5 hours of instrument training to meet the requirements of FAR Part 141, Appendix D.*

POSTFLIGHT DISCUSSION AND PREVIEW OF NEXT LESSON

STAGE VI

STAGE OBJECTIVES

The objective of Stage VI is to provide the instruction and practice necessary to attain the proficiency level required of a commercial pilot with an instrument rating.

STAGE COMPLETION STANDARDS

This stage is complete when the student can demonstrate all flight maneuvers and procedures at the proficiency level of a commercial pilot with an instrument rating. The student also will successfully complete the Stage VI and end-of-course flight checks.

STAGE VI FLIGHT LESSON 68

DUAL — LOCAL

RECOMMENDED SEQUENCE:

1. Preflight Orientation
2. Flight
3. Postflight Evaluation

LESSON OBJECTIVES:

- Full panel instrument procedures are reviewed to maintain the student's instrument scan rate and reinforce the ability to interpret instrument indications.
- Normal and emergency procedures are reviewed to increase judgment and performance.

REVIEW:

FULL PANEL INSTRUMENT

- ❑ Straight-and-Level Flight
- ❑ Standard-Rate Turns
- ❑ Steep Turns
- ❑ Climbs (Constant Airspeed)
- ❑ Descents (Constant Airspeed)
- ❑ Recovery from Unusual Flight Attitudes

TAKEOFFS AND LANDINGS

- ❑ Normal
- ❑ Short-Field Takeoff and Maximum Performance Climb
- ❑ Soft-Field
- ❑ Crosswind
- ❑ Power-Off 180° Accuracy Approach and Landing
- ❑ Go-Around/Rejected Landing

SIMULATED EMERGENCY PROCEDURES

- ❑ Systems and Equipment Malfunctions
- ❑ Emergency Approach and Landing (Simulated)
- ❑ Collision Avoidance
- ❑ Low-Level Wind Shear
- ❑ Wake Turbulence Avoidance

COMPLETION STANDARDS:

- The student's performance and knowledge of each maneuver should meet the minimum standards outlined in the current FAA Commercial Pilot Practical Test Standards.

NOTE: *The instrument portion of this lesson should be accomplished on an as required basis depending on an assessment of the student's capabilities. Students enrolled in the Commercial Pilot Certification Course only must complete 5 hours of instrument training to meet the requirements of FAR Part 141, Appendix D.*

POSTFLIGHT DISCUSSION AND PREVIEW OF NEXT LESSON

STAGE VI FLIGHT LESSON 69

DUAL — LOCAL

RECOMMENDED SEQUENCE:

1. Preflight Orientation
2. Flight
3. Postflight Evaluation

LESSON OBJECTIVES:

- Full and partial panel instrument flight, VOR and NDB navigation, instrument approaches and commercial maneuvers are reviewed in this lesson.
- The student should increase proficiency in instrument maneuvers and procedures. In addition, the student should demonstrate improvement in the performance of the commercial maneuvers.

REVIEW:

FULL AND PARTIAL PANEL INSTRUMENT

- ❑ Straight-and-Level Flight
- ❑ Climbs and Descents
- ❑ Recovery From Unusual Flight Attitudes
- ❑ VOR Orientation and Tracking
- ❑ Nonprecision Approach (Partial Panel)
- ❑ ILS Approach
- ❑ NDB Approach

COMMERCIAL MANEUVERS

- ❑ Steep Turns
- ❑ Chandelles
- ❑ Eights-On-Pylons
- ❑ Steep Spirals

COMPLETION STANDARDS:

- The student's performance during instrument maneuvers and procedures should meet the minimum standards outlined in the current FAA Instrument Pilot Practical Test Standards. Improvement should be evident in the performance of commercial maneuvers.

NOTE: *The instrument portion of this lesson should be accomplished on an as required basis depending on an assessment of the student's capabilities. Students enrolled in the Commercial Pilot Certification Course only must complete 5 hours of instrument training to meet the requirements of FAR Part 141, Appendix D.*

POSTFLIGHT DISCUSSION AND PREVIEW OF NEXT LESSON

STAGE VI FLIGHT LESSONS 70 AND 71

SOLO — LOCAL

LESSON OBJECTIVES:

- Flights 70 and 71 are solo review lessons designed to increase the student's proficiency in commercial maneuvers.

REVIEW:

- ❑ Lazy Eights
- ❑ Eights-On-Pylons
- ❑ Chandelles
- ❑ Steep Turns
- ❑ Steep Spirals

COMPLETION STANDARDS:

- Lessons 70 and 71 are complete when the student has conducted the assigned solo flights.
- During each flight, the student should attempt to perform lazy eights with symmetrical loops and eights-on-pylons, chandelles, steep turns, and steep spirals with smoothness and coordination.

POSTFLIGHT DISCUSSION AND PREVIEW OF NEXT LESSON

STAGE VI FLIGHT LESSON 72

DUAL — LOCAL

RECOMMENDED SEQUENCE:

1. Preflight Orientation
2. Flight
3. Postflight Evaluation

LESSON OBJECTIVES:

- The objective of this lesson is to determine the student's progress in mastery of the commercial maneuvers.
- Correct any areas of faulty performance.

REVIEW:

- ❑ Systems and Equipment Malfunctions
- ❑ Lazy Eights
- ❑ Chandelles
- ❑ Eights-On-Pylons
- ❑ Steep Spirals

COMPLETION STANDARDS:

- The student should demonstrate an understanding of the important performance elements of each maneuver including the correct entry, execution, and recovery techniques.

POSTFLIGHT DISCUSSION AND PREVIEW OF NEXT LESSON

STAGE VI FLIGHT LESSONS 73, 74, AND 75

SOLO — LOCAL

LESSON OBJECTIVES:

- The student should practice each flight maneuver assigned with emphasis on those maneuvers that were poorly or inaccurately performed during the previous dual flight.

REVIEW:

- ❑ Normal Takeoffs and Landings
- ❑ Crosswind Takeoffs and Landings
- ❑ Short-Field Takeoffs/Maximum Performance Climbs and Landings
- ❑ Soft-Field Takeoffs and Landings
- ❑ Power-Off 180° Accuracy Approaches and Landings
- ❑ Maneuvering During Slow Flight
- ❑ Lazy Eights
- ❑ Chandelles
- ❑ Steep Turns
- ❑ Eights-On-Pylons
- ❑ Steep Spirals

COMPLETION STANDARDS:

- Flight Lessons 73, 74, and 75 are complete when the student has accomplished a solo review of each of the listed maneuvers.
- Proficiency should, with few exceptions, meet the minimum standards outlined in the Commercial Pilot PTS.

POSTFLIGHT DISCUSSION AND PREVIEW OF NEXT LESSON

STAGE VI FLIGHT LESSONS 76 AND 77

DUAL — LOCAL

RECOMMENDED SEQUENCE:

1. Preflight Orientation
2. Flight
3. Postflight Evaluation

LESSON OBJECTIVES:

- These lessons provide the student with an opportunity to practice additional commercial maneuvers under instructor supervision to help identify areas where improved performance is necessary.
- Review instrument procedures on an as required basis.

REVIEW:

PREFLIGHT PREPARATIONS AND GROUND OPERATIONS

- ❑ Certificates and Documents
- ❑ Airworthiness Requirements
- ❑ Operation of Systems
- ❑ Performance and Limitations
- ❑ Use of Checklists
- ❑ Preflight Inspection
- ❑ Cockpit Management
- ❑ Engine Starting
- ❑ Taxiing
- ❑ Before Takeoff Check

TAKEOFFS AND LANDINGS

- ❑ Normal and Crosswind Takeoff and Landing
- ❑ Short-Field Takeoff/Maximum Performance Climb and Landing
- ❑ Soft-Field Takeoff and Landing
- ❑ Power-Off 180° Accuracy Approach and Landing

VFR FLIGHT MANEUVERS

- ❑ Maneuvering During Slow Flight
- ❑ Power-Off Stalls
- ❑ Power-On Stalls
- ❑ Chandelles
- ❑ Lazy Eights
- ❑ Eights-On-Pylons
- ❑ Steep Turns
- ❑ Steep Spirals

SIMULATED EMERGENCY PROCEDURES

- ❑ Systems and Equipment Malfunctions
- ❑ Emergency Approach and Landing (Simulated)
- ❑ Go-Around/Rejected Landing

INSTRUMENT PROCEDURES (AS REQUIRED)

POSTFLIGHT PROCEDURES

- ❑ After Landing
- ❑ Parking and Securing

COMPLETION STANDARDS:

- The student should demonstrate familiarity with the flight characteristics, systems, and emergency procedures listed in the lesson.
- Performance of the commercial maneuvers should indicate good understanding of the correct procedures. Maneuvers or procedures which do not meet commercial standards will be assigned for additional practice.
- Demonstrate a high degree of proficiency in assigned instrument procedures.

POSTFLIGHT DISCUSSION AND PREVIEW OF NEXT LESSON

STAGE VI
FLIGHT LESSON 78
DUAL — LOCAL
COMPLEX AIRCRAFT

RECOMMENDED SEQUENCE:

1. Preflight Orientation
2. Flight
3. Postflight Evaluation

LESSON OBJECTIVES:

- This lesson provides the student with an opportunity to practice commercial maneuvers and procedures identified in previous lessons as areas needing review.
- Review maneuvers and procedures in the complex aircraft.

REVIEW:

PREFLIGHT PREPARATIONS AND GROUND OPERATIONS

❑ Certificates and Documents
❑ Airworthiness Requirements
❑ Operation of Systems
❑ Performance and Limitations
❑ Use of Checklists
❑ Preflight Inspection
❑ Cockpit Management
❑ Engine Starting
❑ Taxiing
❑ Before Takeoff Check

TAKEOFFS AND LANDINGS

❑ Normal and Crosswind Takeoff and Landing
❑ Short-Field Takeoff/Maximum Performance Climb and Landing
❑ Soft-Field Takeoff and Landing
❑ Power-Off 180° Accuracy Approach and Landing

VFR FLIGHT MANEUVERS

❑ Maneuvering During Slow Flight
❑ Power-Off Stalls
❑ Power-On Stalls
❑ Chandelles
❑ Lazy Eights
❑ Eights-On-Pylons
❑ Steep Turns
❑ Steep Spirals

SIMULATED EMERGENCY PROCEDURES

❑ Systems and Equipment Malfunctions
❑ Emergency Approach and Landing (Simulated)
❑ Go-Around/Rejected Landing

POSTFLIGHT PROCEDURES

❑ After Landing
❑ Parking and Securing

COMPLETION STANDARDS:

- The student should demonstrate familiarity with the complex aircraft flight characteristics, systems, and emergency procedures assigned in the lesson.
- Performance of the commercial maneuvers should indicate good understanding of the correct procedures. Maneuvers or procedures which do not meet commercial standards will be assigned for additional practice.

POSTFLIGHT DISCUSSION AND PREVIEW OF NEXT LESSON

STUDY ASSIGNMENT:

Review, as required, the necessary information to complete the FAA commercial pilot airmen knowledge test.

STAGE VI FLIGHT LESSONS 79, 80, AND 81

SOLO — LOCAL

LESSON OBJECTIVES:

- During flights 79, 80, and 81, the student should practice the flight maneuvers in order to correct any faulty performance areas from the previous dual flight.

REVIEW:

- ❏ Chandelles
- ❏ Lazy Eights
- ❏ Eights-On-Pylons
- ❏ Steep Turns
- ❏ Steep Spirals
- ❏ Short-Field Takeoffs/Maximum Performance Climbs and Landings
- ❏ Soft-Field Takeoffs and Landings
- ❏ Power-Off 180° Accuracy Approaches and Landings
- ❏ Maneuvering During Slow Flight
- ❏ Power-On Stalls
- ❏ Power-Off Stalls

COMPLETION STANDARDS:

- Flights 79, 80, and 81 are complete when the student has accomplished a solo review of each of the listed maneuvers and has attempted to correct any areas of faulty performance.

POSTFLIGHT DISCUSSION AND PREVIEW OF NEXT LESSON

STAGE VI FLIGHT LESSON 82

DUAL — CROSS-COUNTRY, COMPLEX AIRCRAFT

RECOMMENDED SEQUENCE:

1. Preflight Orientation
2. Flight
3. Postflight Evaluation

LESSON OBJECTIVES:

- This lesson is an evaluation of the student's ability to conduct cross-country flight operations in a complex aircraft. The flight will include a landing at a point more than 50 nautical miles from the original departure point.

REVIEW:

- ❏ Preflight Preparation
- ❏ Cross-Country Flight Planning
- ❏ Weather Information
- ❏ Cockpit Management
- ❏ High Density Altitude Operations

NAVIGATION

- ❏ Navigation Systems and Radar Services
- ❏ Pilotage
- ❏ Dead Reckoning
- ❏ Diversion
- ❏ Lost Procedures
- ❏ Cruise Procedures
- ❏ Power Settings and Mixture Leaning
- ❏ Radio Communications and ATC Light Signals

HIGH ALTITUDE OPERATIONS

- ❏ Supplemental Oxygen
- ❏ Pressurization

SIMULATED EMERGENCY PROCEDURES

- ❏ Systems and Equipment Malfunctions
- ❏ Low Fuel Supply
- ❏ Turbulence
- ❏ Adverse Weather
- ❏ Airframe and Powerplant Icing

UNFAMILIAR AIRPORTS

- ❏ Traffic Patterns
- ❏ UNICOM-Equipped Field
- ❏ Tower-controlled Field
- ❏ Operations at Sod or Unimproved Field
- ❏ CTAF Procedures
- ❏ Airport, Runway, and Taxiway Signs, Markings, and Lighting

FULL PANEL INSTRUMENT

- ❑ Climbs
- ❑ Climbing Turns
- ❑ Descents
- ❑ Descending Turns
- ❑ Standard-Rate Turns
- ❑ Recovery From Unusual Flight Attitudes
- ❑ VOR Navigation
- ❑ NDB Navigation
- ❑ Use of Radar Vectors
- ❑ Radio Facility Shutdown

COMPLETION STANDARDS:

- This lesson is complete when the student demonstrates the ability to safely act as pilot in command of the complex aircraft during cross-country flights.
- In addition, the student will display a basic competency in the associated normal and emergency procedures.

NOTE: *The instrument portion of this lesson should be accomplished on an as required basis depending on an assessment of the student's capabilities. Students enrolled in the Commercial Pilot Certification Course only must complete 5 hours of instrument training to meet the requirements of FAR Part 141, Appendix D.*

POSTFLIGHT DISCUSSION AND PREVIEW OF NEXT LESSON

STUDY ASSIGNMENT:

Begin to review, as necessary, in preparation for the Stage VI Check in Flight Lesson 86.

STAGE VI

FLIGHT LESSON 83

DUAL — LOCAL

COMPLEX AIRCRAFT

RECOMMENDED SEQUENCE:

1. Preflight Orientation
2. Flight
3. Postflight Evaluation

LESSON OBJECTIVES:

- The objective is to determine the student's progress in preparation for the commercial pilot practical test.

REVIEW:

- ❑ Preflight Preparation and Ground Operations
- ❑ Use of Checklists
- ❑ Postflight Procedures

SIMULATED EMERGENCY PROCEDURES

- ❑ Engine Failure
- ❑ Systems and Equipment Malfunctions

FLIGHT MANEUVERS

- ❑ Chandelles
- ❑ Lazy Eights
- ❑ Eights-On-Pylons
- ❑ Steep Turns
- ❑ Steep Spirals
- ❑ Short-Field Takeoffs/Maximum Performance Climbs and Landings
- ❑ Soft-Field Takeoffs and Landings
- ❑ Power-Off 180° Accuracy Approaches and Landings
- ❑ Go-Around/Rejected Landing
- ❑ Flight at Slow Airspeeds
- ❑ Recognition of and Recovery from Stalls Entered from Straight Flight and from Turns

COMPLETION STANDARDS:

- The lesson is complete when the student can perform each of the listed maneuvers and procedures according to the minimum performance standards outlined in the current FAA Commercial Pilot Practical Test Standards.

POSTFLIGHT DISCUSSION AND PREVIEW OF NEXT LESSON

STUDY ASSIGNMENT:

Prepare for the Commercial Pilot Practical Test Briefing for Flight Lessons 84 and 85.

STAGE VI FLIGHT LESSONS 84 AND 85

DUAL — LOCAL

RECOMMENDED SEQUENCE:

1. Preflight Orientation: Briefing — Commercial Pilot Practical Test
2. Flight
3. Postflight Evaluation

LESSON OBJECTIVES:

- Flights 84 and 85 review all the flight maneuvers. Here, the student will gain not only proficiency, but also the confidence and ability to complete the flight test accurately and successfully.

REVIEW:

FLIGHT MANEUVERS

- ❑ Chandelles
- ❑ Lazy Eights
- ❑ Eights-On-Pylons
- ❑ Steep Turns
- ❑ Steep Spirals
- ❑ Maneuvering During Slow Flight
- ❑ Power-Off Stalls
- ❑ Power-On Stalls

TAKEOFFS AND LANDINGS

- ❑ Short-Field Takeoff/Maximum Performance Climb and Landing
- ❑ Soft-Field Takeoff and Landing
- ❑ Crosswind Takeoff and Landing
- ❑ Power-Off 180° Accuracy Approach and Landing

COMPLETION STANDARDS:

- The student will demonstrate proficiency and competence required for commercial pilot certification by performing the outlined maneuvers with smoothness and coordination.
- Performance tolerances should meet or exceed those outlined in the current FAA Commercial Pilot Practical Test Standards.

POSTFLIGHT DISCUSSION AND PREVIEW OF NEXT LESSON

STUDY ASSIGNMENT:

Prepare for the Stage VI Check in Flight Lesson 86 and the end-of-course flight check in Flight Lesson 87.

STAGE VI FLIGHT LESSON 86

DUAL — LOCAL

STAGE VI CHECK

RECOMMENDED SEQUENCE:

1. Preflight Orientation
2. Flight
3. Postflight Evaluation

LESSON OBJECTIVES:

- This stage check, conducted by the chief instructor, assistant chief, or a designated check instructor evaluates the student's ability to perform commercial maneuvers smoothly and precisely.
- The student also will perform VOR, NDB, localizer, and ILS approaches and comply with missed approach procedures according to FAA practical test standards.

NOTE: *The instrument competency portion of this stage check will be conducted on an as required basis. This part of the flight applies to students who are enrolled, in the Instrument/Commercial Course concurrently and have not completed the FAA practical test for the instrument rating.*

REVIEW:

FLIGHT MANEUVERS

- ❑ Chandelles
- ❑ Eights-On-Pylons
- ❑ Steep Turns
- ❑ Steep Spirals
- ❑ Stalls
- ❑ Spin Awareness
- ❑ Maneuvering During Slow Flight

TAKEOFFS AND CLIMBS

- ❏ Normal
- ❏ Crosswind
- ❏ Short-Field/Maximum Performance Climb
- ❏ Soft-Field

APPROACHES AND LANDINGS

- ❏ Normal
- ❏ Crosswind
- ❏ Short-Field
- ❏ Soft-Field
- ❏ Go-Around/Rejected Landing
- ❏ Power-Off 180° Accuracy Approach and Landing

INSTRUMENT PROCEDURES

- ❏ VOR Approaches
- ❏ NDB Approaches
- ❏ Localizer Approaches
- ❏ ILS Approaches
- ❏ Missed Approach Procedures
- ❏ Cockpit Management

POSTFLIGHT PROCEDURES

- ❏ After Landing
- ❏ Parking
- ❏ Securing

COMPLETION STANDARDS:

- During each approach, the student will follow the step-by-step procedure published on the approach chart.
- Descents to the MDA or DH will be at the proper rate, so as to arrive at a position from which a normal circling or straight-in landing can be made. Missed approach procedures will follow the published procedure or the controller's instructions.
- All VFR maneuvers will be performed according to FAA practical test standards.

POSTFLIGHT DISCUSSION AND PREVIEW OF NEXT LESSON

STUDY ASSIGNMENT:

Prepare for the end-of-course flight check for course completion in Flight Lesson 87.

STAGE VI

FLIGHT LESSON 87

DUAL — LOCAL

END-OF-COURSE FLIGHT CHECK FOR COURSE COMPLETION

RECOMMENDED SEQUENCE:

1. Preflight Orientation
2. Flight
3. Postflight Evaluation

LESSON OBJECTIVES:

- This flight check, conducted by the chief instructor, assistant chief instructor, or a designated check instructor, will evaluate the student's instrument and commercial flight proficiency, as well as the ability to act safely and competently as pilot in command.
- The student will be evaluated on their ability to control the aircraft accurately and smoothly while exercising sound judgment in decision making.

NOTE: *The instrument competency portion of this stage check will be conducted on an as required basis. This part of the flight applies to students who are enrolled, in the Instrument/Commercial Course concurrently and have not completed the FAA practical test for the instrument rating.*

REVIEW:

IFR CROSS-COUNTRY FLIGHT PLANNING

- ❏ Weather Information
- ❏ Cockpit Management
- ❏ Filing an IFR Flight Plan
- ❏ IFR Preflight Inspection
- ❏ IFR Takeoff Preparations
- ❏ Obtaining an IFR Clearance
- ❏ IFR Departure Procedures
- ❏ Voice Communications

- ❑ Enroute Procedures
- ❑ Aeronautical Decision Making

VOR

- ❑ Orientation
- ❑ Interception
- ❑ Tracking
- ❑ VOR Holding

NDB

- ❑ Orientation
- ❑ Interception
- ❑ Tracking
- ❑ NDB Holding

ARRIVAL PROCEDURES

- ❑ ILS Approach
- ❑ VOR and/or VOR/DME Approaches
- ❑ NDB Approach
- ❑ Radar Approach
- ❑ Missed Approach

SIMULATED EMERGENCY PROCEDURES

- ❑ Loss of Communications
- ❑ Radio Failure
- ❑ Instrument Failure
- ❑ Engine Failure
- ❑ Systems and Equipment Malfunctions

FLIGHT MANEUVERS

- ❑ Chandelles
- ❑ Lazy Eights
- ❑ Eights-On-Pylons
- ❑ Steep Turns
- ❑ Steep Spirals
- ❑ Short-Field Takeoffs/Maximum Performance Climbs and Landings
- ❑ Soft-Field Takeoffs and Landings
- ❑ Go-Around/Rejected Landing
- ❑ Flight at Slow Airspeeds
- ❑ Recognition of and Recovery from Stalls Entered from Straight Flight and from Turns

POSTFLIGHT PROCEDURES

- ❑ After Landing
- ❑ Parking
- ❑ Securing

COMPLETION STANDARDS:

- At the completion of this flight check, the student will display a complete understanding of VFR and IFR procedures. The student also will demonstrate the necessary knowledge, skill, and judgment to operate safely as pilot in command.
- The student's performance during each maneuver and procedure will exceed the minimum performance requirements outlined in the current FAA Instrument and Commercial Pilot Practical Test Standards.

POSTFLIGHT DISCUSSION

NOTE: *If the student has not taken the FAA instrument rating practical test, the Instrument Rating Practical Test Briefing also should be used during this Flight Lesson.*

MULTI-ENGINE PILOT STAGE VI

STAGE OBJECTIVES

During this stage, the student will learn multi-engine aerodynamics, operating procedures, systems, and performance considerations. The applicant will learn to accurately use performance charts and compute weight and balance data to control the weight and balance conditions of the multi-engine airplane. In addition, the student will learn principles, techniques, and procedures which apply to engine-out and instrument flight in the multi-engine airplane.

STAGE COMPLETION STANDARDS

This stage is complete when the student has passed the Stage VI Exam and the Multi-Engine End-of-Course Exam with a minimum score of 80%, and the instructor has reviewed each incorrect response to ensure complete understanding.

NOTE: Ground Training Lessons are based on the GFD Multi-Engine textbook *(JS314540)*

STAGE VI GROUND LESSON 1

LESSON REFERENCES:

MULTI-ENGINE TEXTBOOK
Chapter 1, Exploring the Multi-Engine Rating, and Chapter 4, Performing Maneuvers and Procedures, Section A — Normal Operations

MULTI-ENGINE RATING VIDEO
Volume 1 — Multi-Engine Operations

RECOMMENDED SEQUENCE:

1. Lesson Introduction and Video Presentation
2. Class Discussion

LESSON OBJECTIVES:

- During this lesson, the student will become familiar with the training program and applicable regulations.
- The student will learn basic human factors concepts as they relate to multi-engine operations, including high-altitude physiology.
- The student will be introduced to the training airplane and to the procedures relating to normal operations in a multi-engine airplane, including normal and short-field takeoff and landing procedures.

ACADEMIC CONTENT:

CHAPTER 1 — EXPLORING THE MULTI-ENGINE RATING

SECTION A — SEEKING A NEW EXPERIENCE

❑ Why a Multi-Engine Rating?
❑ The Training Path

SECTION B — CONSIDERING HUMAN FACTORS

❑ Multi-Engine Safety
❑ PIC Responsibility
❑ Communication
❑ Resource Use
❑ Workload Management
❑ Situational Awareness
❑ High-Altitude Physiology

CHAPTER 4 — PERFORMING MANEUVERS AND PROCEDURES

SECTION A – NORMAL OPERATIONS

❑ Using Checklists
❑ Preflight Inspection (Including Airworthiness Requirements)
❑ Ground Operations
  - Engine Starting
  - Taxiing
  - Before-Takeoff Check
❑ Takeoff and Climb
❑ Short-Field Takeoff and Maximum Performance Climb
❑ Cruising and Descent Planning
❑ Approach and Landing

- ❑ Short-Field Approach and Landing
- ❑ Go-Around

COMPLETION STANDARDS:

- During oral quizzing by the instructor, the student will demonstrate understanding of the training program and the human factors issues related to multi-engine operations.
- The student will exhibit knowledge of normal operating procedures by explaining elements selected by the instructor.
- The student will review the Summary Checklists and Key Terms for Chapter 1, Sections A and B, and complete Exercise 4A with a minimum passing score of 80%. The instructor will review each incorrect response to ensure complete understanding before progressing to Ground Lesson 2.

STUDY ASSIGNMENT:

MULTI-ENGINE TEXTBOOK
Chapter 2, Understanding Your Airplane

STAGE VI GROUND LESSON 2

LESSON REFERENCES:

MULTI-ENGINE TEXTBOOK
Chapter 2, Understanding Your Airplane

RECOMMENDED SEQUENCE:

1. Lesson Introduction
2. Class Discussion

LESSON OBJECTIVES:

- The student will become familiar with the equipment and systems of the training airplane and learn how to compute and control the weight and balance. The student will also learn to accurately determine aircraft performance from multi-engine airplane performance tables, charts, and/or graphs.

ACADEMIC CONTENT:

CHAPTER 2 — UNDERSTANDING YOUR AIRPLANE

SECTION A — EXAMINING SYSTEMS

- ❑ Multi-Engine Powerplant Systems
  - Fuel Metering Systems
  - Ignition and Starting Systems
  - Lubrication Systems
  - Induction Systems
  - Cooling and Exhaust Systems
  - Engine Indicating Systems
- ❑ Engine-Driven Power Systems
  - Electrical Generating Systems
  - Pneumatic Power Systems
  - Hydraulic Power Systems
- ❑ Propeller Systems
  - Constant-Speed Operations
  - Power Control
  - Propeller Synchronizing
  - Feathering
  - Restarting
- ❑ Multi-Engine Airframe Systems
  - Electrical Distribution
  - Hydraulic Systems
  - Fuel Systems
  - Landing Gear Systems
  - Ice and Rain Control Systems
  - Cabin Environmental Systems

SECTION B — CALCULATING WEIGHT AND BALANCE

- ❑ Weight Considerations
- ❑ Balance Considerations
- ❑ Weight Shifts
- ❑ Calculating Weight and Balance

SECTION C — DETERMINING PERFORMANCE

- ❑ Performance Definitions
- ❑ The Engine-Out Performance Penalty
- ❑ Using Performance Data
- ❑ V-Speeds
- ❑ Takeoff and Climb
  - Single-Engine Rate of Climb
  - Accelerate-Stop Distance
  - Accelerate-Go Distance
  - Climb
- ❑ Cruise Flight
  - Single-Engine Ceilings
- ❑ Descent
- ❑ Landing Performance Calculations
- ❑ Engine-Out Go-Around

COMPLETION STANDARDS:

- The student will exhibit knowledge of the systems of the training airplane by explaining the operation of relevant systems.

- The student will demonstrate the ability to correctly compute the weight and balance for the training airplane, including the expected performance based on at least two different loading conditions with the airport and environmental conditions as specified by the instructor.

The student will complete Exercises 2A, 2B, and 2C with a minimum passing score of 80%, and the instructor will review each incorrect response to ensure complete understanding before progressing to Ground Lesson 3.

STUDY ASSIGNMENT:

MULTI-ENGINE TEXTBOOK
Chapter 3, Discovering Aerodynamics and Chapter 4, Section B — Maneuvers

STAGE VI GROUND LESSON 3

LESSON REFERENCES:

MULTI-ENGINE TEXTBOOK
Chapter 3, Discovering Aerodynamics and Chapter 4, Section B — Maneuvers

MULTI-ENGINE RATING VIDEO
Volume 1 — Multi-Engine Aerodynamics and Multi-Engine Maneuvers

RECOMMENDED SEQUENCE:

1. Lesson Introduction and Video Presentation
2. Class Discussion

LESSON OBJECTIVES:

- During this lesson, the student will learn the fundamentals of multi-engine and engine-out aerodynamics and the elements of the specified multi-engine maneuvers.
- The student will also develop stall/spin awareness and a clear understanding of the elements relating to stalls and spins in multi-engine airplanes.

ACADEMIC CONTENT:

CHAPTER 3 — DISCOVERING AERODYNAMICS

SECTION A — INTRODUCING MULTI-ENGINE AERODYNAMICS

❑ Boundary Layer
❑ Induced Flow
❑ Turning Tendencies
❑ High-Speed Flight

SECTION B — MASTERING ENGINE-OUT AERODYNAMICS

❑ Engine Failure
❑ Yaw and Roll
❑ Critical Engine
❑ Cure for Yaw and Roll
❑ V_{MC}
❑ Windmilling Propeller
❑ Feathering
❑ Sideslip
❑ Controllability vs. Performance
- Weight
- Angle of Bank
- Center of Gravity
- Power

CHAPTER 4 — PERFORMING MANEUVERS AND PROCEDURES

SECTION B — MANEUVERS

❑ Steep Turns
❑ Slow Flight
❑ Stalls (Power-On and Power-Off)
❑ Spin Awareness
❑ Emergency Descent

COMPLETION STANDARDS:

- The student will demonstrate knowledge of multi-engine aerodynamics by explaining elements selected by the instructor during oral quizzing.
- The student will demonstrate knowledge of the required maneuvers by explaining the elements relating to each maneuver.
- The student will demonstrate knowledge of stalls and spins in multi-engine airplanes by explaining the aerodynamic conditions required for a spin, the flight situations and conditions where unintentional spins may

occur, the instrument indications during a spin and/or spiral, and the techniques and procedures used to recognize and recover from unintentional spins.

The student will complete Exercises 3A, 3B, and 4B with a minimum passing score of 80%, and the instructor will review each incorrect response to ensure complete understanding before progressing to Ground Lesson 4.

STUDY ASSIGNMENT:

MULTI-ENGINE TEXTBOOK
Chapter 5, Section A — When an Engine Fails and Section B — Engine-Out Maneuvers

STAGE VI GROUND LESSON 4

LESSON REFERENCES:

MULTI-ENGINE TEXTBOOK
Chapter 5, Section A — When an Engine Fails and Section B — Engine-Out Maneuvers

MULTI-ENGINE RATING VIDEO
Volume I, Engine-Out Operations

RECOMMENDED SEQUENCE:

1. Lesson Introduction and Video Presentation
2. Class Discussion

LESSON OBJECTIVE:

- During this lesson, the student will learn the procedures and maneuvers relating to engine-out operations in multi-engine airplanes.

ACADEMIC CONTENT:

CHAPTER 5 — MASTERING ENGINE-OUT OPERATIONS

SECTION A — WHEN AN ENGINE FAILS

❑ Taking Action
- Pitch
- Power
- Drag
- Identify
- Verify
- Troubleshoot

❑ Feathering
- After Actual Engine Failure
- During Training
- Restarting the Engine

❑ Establish a Bank
❑ Securing the Inoperative Engine
❑ Monitoring the Operative Engine

SECTION B — ENGINE-OUT MANEUVERS

❑ Takeoff and Climb (Loss of Engine Power Before V_{MC} and After Liftoff)
❑ Enroute
❑ V_{MC} Demonstration
❑ Drag Demonstration
❑ Landing
❑ Engine-Out Go-Around

COMPLETION STANDARDS:

- The student will demonstrate the ability to properly accomplish the appropriate checklists, operate the airplane safely during engine-inoperative flight, make appropriate decisions regarding the continuation of flight, and accomplish the required procedures and maneuvers within the limits established by the Practical Test Standards.

- The student will complete Exercises 5A and 5B with a minimum passing score of 80%, and the instructor will review each incorrect response to ensure complete understanding before progressing to Ground Lesson 5.

STUDY ASSIGNMENT:

MULTI-ENGINE TEXTBOOK
Chapter 5, Section C — Operating on Instruments and Section D — Making Decisions

STAGE VI GROUND LESSON 5

LESSON REFERENCES:

MULTI-ENGINE TEXTBOOK
Chapter 5, Section C — Operating on Instruments and Section D — Making Decisions

MULTI-ENGINE RATING VIDEO
Volume I, Instrument Operations

RECOMMENDED SEQUENCE:

1. Lesson Introduction and Video Presentation
2. Class Discussion

LESSON OBJECTIVE:

- During this lesson, the student will acquire the knowledge of instrument procedures in the multi-engine airplane with both engines operating and with one engine inoperative.
- The student will become familiar with critical decision-making processes involving flight in multi-engine airplanes.

ACADEMIC CONTENT:

CHAPTER 5 — MASTERING ENGINE-OUT OPERATIONS

SECTION C — OPERATING ON INSTRUMENTS

❑ Attitude Instrument Flying
❑ Departure
❑ Enroute
❑ Engine-Out Instrument Approach

SECTION D – MAKING DECISIONS

❑ Applying the Decision-Making Process
❑ PIC Responsibility
❑ Communication
❑ Resource Use
❑ Workload Management
❑ Situational Awareness
❑ Controlled Flight Into Terrain (CFIT)
❑ Poor Judgment Chain

COMPLETION STANDARDS:

- The student will demonstrate knowledge of the additional considerations involved in planning and executing a flight under IFR in a multi-engine airplane during oral quizzing by the instructor.
- The student will demonstrate knowledge of engine-out operations in IFR conditions, by explaining elements selected by the instructor.
- The student will demonstrate understanding of the concepts and factors of decision making in a multi-engine airplane during oral quizzing by the instructor.
- The student will complete Exercises 5C and 5D with a minimum passing score of 80%, and the instructor will review each incorrect response to ensure complete understanding before progressing to Ground Lesson 6.

STUDY ASSIGNMENT:

MULTI-ENGINE TEXTBOOK
Chapters 1, 2, 3, 4, and 5 in preparation for the Stage VI Exam.

STAGE VI GROUND LESSON 6

STAGE VI EXAM

LESSON REFERENCES:

MULTI-ENGINE TEXTBOOK
Chapters 1, 2, 3, 4, and 5

MULTI-ENGINE RATING VIDEO

RECOMMENDED SEQUENCE:

1. Lesson Introduction
2. Testing
3. Critique

LESSON OBJECTIVES:

- Evaluate the student's comprehension of material presented in the *Multi-Engine* textbook Chapters 1, 2, 3, 4, and 5

ACADEMIC CONTENT:

STAGE VI EXAM

- ❑ Multi-Engine Operations and Systems
- ❑ Multi-Engine Aerodynamics
- ❑ Performance Considerations
- ❑ Weight and Balance
- ❑ Performance Charts
- ❑ Engine-Out Operations
- ❑ Multi-Engine Instrument Flight

COMPLETION STANDARDS:

- The lesson and stage are complete when the student has passed the Stage VI Exam with a minimum score of 80%, and the instructor has reviewed each incorrect response to ensure complete understanding before the student progress to the Multi-Engine End-of-Course Exam.

STUDY ASSIGNMENT:

MULTI-ENGINE TEXTBOOK
Review chapters 1, 2, 3, 4, and 5 in preparation for Multi-Engine End-of-Course Exam.

STAGE VI GROUND LESSON 7 END-OF-COURSE EXAM

LESSON REFERENCES:

MULTI-ENGINE TEXTBOOK
Chapters 1, 2, 3, 4, and 5

MULTI-ENGINE RATING VIDEO

RECOMMENDED SEQUENCE:

1. Lesson Introduction
2. Testing
3. Critique

LESSON OBJECTIVES:

- Administer the end-of-course exam covering the material presented in the Multi-Engine Course.

ACADEMIC CONTENT:

- ❑ Multi-Engine Operations and Systems
- ❑ Multi-Engine Aerodynamics
- ❑ Performance Considerations
- ❑ Performance Charts
- ❑ Weight and Balance
- ❑ Engine-Out Operations
- ❑ Multi-Engine Instrument Flight

COMPLETION STANDARDS:

- The lesson and stage are complete when the student has passed the Multi-Engine End-of-Course Exam with a minimum passing score of 80%, and the instructor has reviewed each incorrect response to ensure complete understanding.

MULTI-ENGINE PILOT STAGE VII

STAGE OBJECTIVES

The objective of Stage VII is to provide the instruction and practice necessary to attain the proficiency level required of a multi-engine rated pilot. The student will learn to fly the multi-engine airplane during normal two-engine operations as well as in engine-out situations. Additionally, the student will acquire the proficiency required for IFR operations in the multi-engine airplane.

STAGE COMPLETION STANDARDS

This stage is complete when the student can demonstrate all multi-engine flight maneuvers and procedures at the proficiency level of a commercial pilot with an instrument rating. The student also will successfully complete the Stage VII and end-of-course flight checks.

STAGE VII FLIGHT LESSON 1

DUAL — LOCAL

RECOMMENDED SEQUENCE:

NOTE: *Prior to this flight the student should complete Ground Lesson 1.*

1. Preflight Orientation: Briefing — Multi-Engine Operations and Systems
2. Flight
3. Postflight Evaluation

LESSON OBJECTIVES:

- During the lesson the student will become acquainted with the training airplane.
- The student should learn the attitudes, power settings, and configurations required for the performance of the listed maneuvers and procedures using visual references (VR) and instrument references (IR).

INTRODUCE:

PREFLIGHT PREPARATION

❏ Certificates and Documents
❏ Airworthiness Requirements
❏ Multi-Engine Operation of Systems
❏ Multi-Engine Performance and Limitations
❏ Review of V-Speeds

PREFLIGHT PROCEDURES

❏ Preflight Inspection
❏ Cockpit Management
❏ Engine Starting
❏ Normal and Crosswind Taxiing
❏ Before Takeoff Check

SAFETY-RELATED OPERATIONS AND PROCEDURES

❏ Checklist Usage
❏ Crew Resource Management
❏ Positive Exchange of Flight Controls
❏ Stall/Spin Awareness
❏ Wake Turbulence Avoidance
❏ Low Level Wind Shear
❏ Visual Scanning and Collision Avoidance
❏ Runway Incursion Avoidance
❏ Land and Hold Short Operations (LAHSO)

BASIC INSTRUMENT MANEUVERS (VR) (IR)

❏ Straight-and-Level Flight
❏ Constant Altitude Change of Airspeed
❏ Constant Airspeed Climbs and Descents
❏ Turns to Headings
❏ Drag Changes for Various Configurations

TAKEOFFS AND LANDINGS

❏ Normal Takeoff and Climb
❏ Crosswind Takeoff and Climb
❏ Traffic Patterns
❏ Normal Approach and Landing
❏ Crosswind Approach and Landing

POSTFLIGHT PROCEDURES

❏ After Landing
❏ Parking and Securing

COMPLETION STANDARDS:

- At the completion of this lesson, the student will be able to perform the listed ground operations with a minimum of instructor assistance.
- The applicant will demonstrate the knowledge of attitudes, power settings, and configurations necessary to perform the listed maneuvers and procedures by maintaining altitude ±200 feet, heading ±10°, and airspeed ±10 knots.

POSTFLIGHT DISCUSSION AND PREVIEW OF NEXT LESSON

STUDY ASSIGNMENT:

GROUND LESSON 2 —
Aircraft Systems, Weight and Balance, and Performance

Prepare for the Multi-Engine Performance Considerations Briefing to be given prior to Flight Lesson 2.

STAGE VII
FLIGHT LESSON 2

DUAL — LOCAL

RECOMMENDED SEQUENCE:

1. Preflight Orientation: Briefing — Multi-Engine Performance Considerations
2. Flight
3. Postflight Evaluation

LESSON OBJECTIVES:

- During this lesson, the student will review maneuvers from Flight Lesson 1.
- The student will be introduced to stalls, maneuvering during slow flight, steep turns, and emergency operations to become familiar with the flight characteristics of the multi-engine aircraft.

REVIEW:

PREFLIGHT PREPARATION

- ❑ Certificates and Documents
- ❑ Airworthiness Requirements
- ❑ Multi-Engine Operation of Systems
- ❑ Multi-Engine Performance and Limitations

NORMAL PROCEDURES

- ❑ Preflight Inspection
- ❑ Cockpit Management
- ❑ Engine Starting
- ❑ Normal and Crosswind Taxiing
- ❑ Before Takeoff Check
- ❑ Normal Takeoff and Climb
- ❑ Crosswind Takeoff and Climb
- ❑ Traffic Patterns

SAFETY-RELATED OPERATIONS AND PROCEDURES

- ❑ Checklist Usage
- ❑ Crew Resource Management
- ❑ Positive Exchange of Flight Controls
- ❑ Stall/Spin Awareness
- ❑ Wake Turbulence Avoidance
- ❑ Low Level Wind Shear
- ❑ Visual Scanning and Collision Avoidance
- ❑ Runway Incursion Avoidance

BASIC INSTRUMENT MANEUVERS (VR) (IR)

- ❑ Straight-and-Level Flight
- ❑ Constant Altitude Change of Airspeed
- ❑ Constant Airspeed Climbs and Descents
- ❑ Turns to Headings
- ❑ Drag Changes for Various Configurations
- ❑ Normal Approach and Landing
- ❑ Crosswind Approach and Landing

POSTFLIGHT PROCEDURES

- ❑ After Landing
- ❑ Parking and Securing

INTRODUCE:

- ❑ Maneuvering During Slow Flight
- ❑ Power-On Stalls
- ❑ Power-Off Stalls
- ❑ Steep Turns

EMERGENCY OPERATIONS

- ❑ Emergency Descent
- ❑ Systems and Equipment Malfunctions
- ❑ Emergency Equipment and Survival Gear

COMPLETION STANDARDS:

- At the completion of this lesson, the student will be able to perform the listed ground operations without instructor assistance.
- During takeoff and landing, the applicant will demonstrate good directional control and maintain liftoff, climb, approach, and touchdown airspeed ±10 knots of the correct speed. Straight-and-level flight, climbs, and descents will be performed while maintaining assigned airspeed ±10 knots, rollouts from turns ±10° of assigned heading, and specified altitude ±150 feet.
- The student will be able to demonstrate the correct flight procedures for maneuvering during slow flight, steep turns, emergency descents, and the correct entry and recovery procedures for stalls. Slow flight maneuvers and stalls must be completed no lower than 3,000 feet AGL or the manufacturer's recommended altitude, whichever is higher.

POSTFLIGHT DISCUSSION AND PREVIEW OF NEXT LESSON

STAGE VII FLIGHT LESSON 3

DUAL — LOCAL

RECOMMENDED SEQUENCE:

1. Preflight Orientation
2. Flight
3. Postflight Evaluation

LESSON OBJECTIVES:

- Practice the review maneuvers and procedures to increase proficiency and experience.
- The student will be introduced to short-field takeoffs and maximum performance climbs, short-field approaches and landings, go-arounds, and high altitude operations.

REVIEW:

- ❑ Preflight Procedures
- ❑ Multi-Engine Operations
- ❑ Normal Takeoff and Climb
- ❑ Crosswind Takeoff and Climb
- ❑ Basic Instrument Maneuvers
- ❑ Maneuvering During Slow Flight
- ❑ Power-On Stalls
- ❑ Power-Off Stalls
- ❑ Steep Turns
- ❑ Normal Approach and Landing
- ❑ Crosswind Approach and Landing

SAFETY-RELATED OPERATIONS AND PROCEDURES

- ❑ Checklist Usage
- ❑ Crew Resource Management
- ❑ Positive Exchange of Flight Controls
- ❑ Stall/Spin Awareness
- ❑ Wake Turbulence Avoidance
- ❑ Low Level Wind Shear
- ❑ Visual Scanning and Collision Avoidance
- ❑ Runway Incursion Avoidance
- ❑ Land and Hold Short Operations (LAHSO)

EMERGENCY OPERATIONS

- ❑ Emergency Descent
- ❑ Systems and Equipment Malfunctions
- ❑ Emergency Equipment and Survival Gear

POSTFLIGHT PROCEDURES

- ❑ After Landing
- ❑ Parking and Securing

INTRODUCE:

- ❑ Short-Field Takeoff and Maximum Performance Climb
- ❑ Short-Field Approach and Landing
- ❑ Go-Around/Rejected Landing
- ❑ High Altitude Operations
- ❑ Supplemental Oxygen
- ❑ Pressurization

COMPLETION STANDARDS:

- At the completion of this lesson, the student will perform all the maneuvers and procedures listed for review at a proficiency level that meets or exceeds the criteria set forth in the multi-engine land sections of the current FAA Commercial Pilot Practical Test Standards.
- The student will demonstrate the newly introduced maneuvers and procedures using correct operating techniques, coordination, smoothness, and understanding.

POSTFLIGHT DISCUSSION AND PREVIEW OF NEXT LESSON

STUDY ASSIGNMENT:

GROUND LESSON 3 —

Multi-Engine/Engine-Out Aerodynamics and Maneuvers
Prepare for the Engine-Out Operations Briefing to be given prior to Flight Lesson 4.

STAGE VII FLIGHT LESSON 4

DUAL — LOCAL

RECOMMENDED SEQUENCE:

1. Preflight Orientation: Briefing — Engine-Out Operations
2. Flight
3. Postflight Evaluation

LESSON OBJECTIVES:

- During the lesson, the applicant will practice the review maneuvers and procedures to maintain or gain proficiency.
- The student will be introduced to engine-out procedures and will learn to identify the inoperative engine, initiate appropriate corrective procedures, and maneuver the airplane with one engine inoperative.
- The instructor will conduct the V_{MC} demonstration and recovery so the applicant may learn the significance of the relationship of V_{MC} to stall speed.

REVIEW:

❑ Preflight Procedures
❑ Multi-Engine Operations
❑ Takeoffs and Landings
❑ Go-Arounds/Rejected Landings
❑ Traffic Patterns
❑ Basic Instrument Maneuvers
❑ Slow Flight and Stalls
❑ Postflight Procedures
❑ High Altitude Operations
❑ Steep Turns

INTRODUCE:

EMERGENCY OPERATIONS (ENGINE-OUT)

❑ Flight Principles — Engine-Inoperative
❑ Engine Failure During Cruise
❑ Identification of Inoperative Engine
❑ Procedures for Shutdown and Feathering
❑ Use of Controls to Counteract Yaw and Roll
❑ V_{MC} Demonstration (by Instructor)

NOTE: *The V_{MC} demonstration must be completed no lower than 3,000 feet AGL or the manufacturer's recommended altitude, whichever is higher. In addition, it is imperative that instructors observe precautions applicable to the airplane being flown, particularly limitations associated with high density altitude conditions. In some high density altitude situations, the demonstration may not be practical and should not be attempted.*

MANEUVERING WITH ONE ENGINE INOPERATIVE

❑ Straight-and-Level Flight (VR) (IR)
❑ Turns in Both Directions (VR) (IR)
❑ Climbs and Descents to Assigned Altitudes
❑ Effects of Various Airspeeds and Configurations During Engine Inoperative Performance

COMPLETION STANDARDS:

- At the completion of this lesson, the student will be able to identify the inoperative engine during cruise and use the correct control inputs to maintain straight flight.
- The student should have a complete and accurate knowledge of the cause, effect, and significance of engine-out minimum control speed (V_{MC}) and recognize the imminent loss of control.
- The student will demonstrate the newly introduced maneuvers and procedures using correct operating techniques, coordination, smoothness, and understanding.

POSTFLIGHT DISCUSSION AND PREVIEW OF NEXT LESSON

STUDY ASSIGNMENT:

GROUND LESSON 4 —

Engine-Out Operations

STAGE VII FLIGHT LESSON 5

DUAL — LOCAL

RECOMMENDED SEQUENCE:

1. Preflight Orientation
2. Flight
3. Postflight Evaluation

LESSON OBJECTIVES:

- During the lesson, the student will practice the review maneuvers and procedures to maintain or gain proficiency.
- The student will be introduced to engine failure on takeoff and initial climb as well as approaches and landings with an inoperative engine.
- The student will conduct the V_{MC} demonstration and the proper recovery.

REVIEW:

EMERGENCY OPERATIONS (ENGINE-OUT)

- ❑ Flight Principles — Engine-Inoperative
- ❑ Engine Failure During Cruise
- ❑ Identification of Inoperative Engine
- ❑ Procedures for Shutdown and Feathering
- ❑ Use of Controls to Counteract Yaw and Roll

MANEUVERING WITH ONE ENGINE INOPERATIVE

- ❑ Straight-and-Level Flight (VR) (IR)
- ❑ Turns in Both Directions (VR) (IR)
- ❑ Climbs and Descents to Assigned Altitudes
- ❑ Effects of Various Airspeeds and Configurations During Engine Inoperative Performance

INTRODUCE:

EMERGENCY OPERATIONS (ENGINE-OUT)

- ❑ Engine Failure During Takeoff Before V_{MC} (Simulated)
- ❑ Engine Failure After Liftoff (Simulated)
- ❑ V_{MC} Demonstration
- ❑ Full Feather and Inflight Restart
- ❑ Approach and Landing with an Inoperative Engine (Simulated)

NOTE: *The V_{MC} demonstration must be completed no lower than 3,000 feet AGL or the manufacturer's recommended altitude, whichever is higher. In addition, it is imperative that instructors observe precautions applicable to the airplane being flown, particularly limitations associated with high density altitude conditions. In some high density altitude situations, the demonstration may not be practical and should not be attempted.*

COMPLETION STANDARDS:

- The student will be able to maneuver the airplane during level flight with one engine inoperative, while maintaining altitude ±150 feet and heading ±15°.
- During engine-out climbs, airspeed will be maintained within 5 knots of, but never below, that recommended by the manufacturer.
- The student will promptly identify the inoperative engine and demonstrate correct shutdown and feathering procedures during simulated engine failures.
- The student should have a complete and accurate knowledge of the cause, effect, and significance of engine-out minimum control speed (V_{MC}) and demonstrate the correct procedure for engine failure on takeoff before and after liftoff.
- The student will demonstrate the newly introduced maneuvers and engine-out approach and landing procedures using correct operating techniques, coordination, smoothness, and understanding. Special emphasis should be on maintaining the airspeed within 10 knots of, but never below, the recommended speed.

POSTFLIGHT DISCUSSION AND PREVIEW OF NEXT LESSON

STAGE VII FLIGHT LESSON 6

DUAL — LOCAL

RECOMMENDED SEQUENCE:

1. Preflight Orientation
2. Flight
3. Postflight Evaluation

LESSON OBJECTIVES:

- During the lesson, the student will practice the listed procedures to gain proficiency in engine-out operations.

REVIEW:

- ❑ Short-Field Takeoff and Maximum Performance Climb
- ❑ Short-Field Approach and Landing
- ❑ Basic Instrument Maneuvers

EMERGENCY OPERATIONS (ENGINE-OUT)

- ❑ Engine Failure During Takeoff Before V_{MC} (Simulated)
- ❑ Engine Failure After Liftoff (Simulated)
- ❑ Flight Principles – Engine Inoperative
- ❑ Maneuvering with One Engine Inoperative
- ❑ V_{MC} Demonstration (by Student)
- ❑ Full Feather and Inflight Restart
- ❑ Approach and Landing with an Inoperative Engine (Simulated)

COMPLETION STANDARDS:

- At the completion of this lesson, the student will be able to identify the inoperative engine during cruise and use the correct control inputs to maintain straight and level flight.
- The student should have a complete and accurate knowledge of the cause, effect, and significance of engine-out minimum control speed (V_{MC}) and recognize the imminent loss of control.
- The student will demonstrate the newly introduced maneuvers and procedures using correct operating techniques, coordination, smoothness, and understanding.

POSTFLIGHT DISCUSSION AND PREVIEW OF NEXT LESSON

STUDY ASSIGNMENT:

GROUND LESSON 5 —

Multi-Engine Instrument Flight and Decision Making. Prepare for the Multi-Engine Instrument Flight Briefing to be given prior to Flight Lesson 7.

STAGE VII FLIGHT LESSON 7

DUAL — LOCAL

RECOMMENDED SEQUENCE:

1. Preflight Orientation: Briefing — Multi-Engine Instrument Flight
2. Flight
3. Postflight Evaluation

LESSON OBJECTIVES:

- During the lesson, the student will practice the listed procedures to gain proficiency in engine-out operations with instrument and visual reference.
- The student will be introduced to instrument approaches, missed approach procedures, and holding with all engines operating.

REVIEW:

EMERGENCY OPERATIONS (ENGINE-OUT)

- ❑ Engine Failure During Takeoff Before (V_{MC}) (Simulated)
- ❑ Engine Failure After Liftoff (Simulated)
- ❑ Flight Principles — Engine Inoperative
- ❑ Maneuvering with One Engine Inoperative
- ❑ V_{MC} Demonstration (by Student)
- ❑ Full Feather and Inflight Restart
- ❑ Approach and Landing with an Inoperative Engine (Simulated)

INTRODUCE:

INSTRUMENT APPROACHES — ALL ENGINES OPERATING

- ❑ NDB Approach
- ❑ VOR and/or Localizer Approach
- ❑ ILS Approach

❏ Approach Procedure to Straight-In Minimums
❏ Approach Procedure to Circling Minimums
❏ Missed Approach Considerations

INSTRUMENT PROCEDURES

❏ VOR Holding
❏ NDB Holding
❏ VOR Time and Distance
❏ Intercepting and Tracking DME Arcs (If Airplane So Equipped)

COMPLETION STANDARDS:

- At the completion of this lesson, the student will be able to identify the inoperative engine during cruise and use the correct control inputs to maintain heading ±10° at all times.
- The student should have a complete and accurate knowledge of the cause, effect, and significance of engine-out minimum control speed (V_{MC}) and recognize the imminent loss of control while maintaining airspeed within 5 knots of, but never below, the assigned speed.
- The student will demonstrate the proper control usage, flap and landing gear cleanup procedures, accurate engine shutdown, and correct feathering procedures. Control of the airplane will never be in doubt.
- The student will demonstrate the newly introduced maneuvers and procedures using correct operating techniques, coordination, smoothness, and understanding.

POSTFLIGHT DISCUSSION AND PREVIEW OF NEXT LESSON

STAGE VII
FLIGHT LESSON 8
DUAL — CROSS-COUNTRY, DAY CONDITIONS UNDER VFR

RECOMMENDED SEQUENCE:

1. Preflight Orientation
2. Flight
3. Postflight Evaluation

LESSON OBJECTIVES:

- During this session, the student will review procedures and maneuvers that require additional practice from the prior lesson.
- The student should gain additional proficiency in basic instrument flight operations during a planned cross-country flight.
- The applicant will be introduced to engine-out maneuvers and procedures during simulated instrument flight.

REVIEW:

MANEUVERS (AS REQUIRED)

INTRODUCE:

CROSS-COUNTRY FLIGHT PLANNING

❏ Navigation Systems and Radar Services
❏ Pilotage and Dead Reckoning
❏ Lost Procedures
❏ Diversion
❏ Weather Information
❏ National Airspace System
❏ Aeromedical Factors
❏ Radio Communications and ATC Light Signals
❏ Airport, Runway, and Taxiway Signs, Markings, and Lighting

BASIC INSTRUMENT MANEUVERS

❏ Straight-and-Level Flight
❏ Constant Airspeed Climbs and Descents
❏ Constant Rate Climbs and Descents
❏ Turns to Headings
❏ Magnetic Compass Turns
❏ Situational/Positional Awareness

PERFORMANCE MANEUVERS (IR)

❏ Identification of Inoperative Engine
❏ Procedures for Shutdown and Feathering
❏ Engine Failure During Climbs

- ❑ Engine Failure During Straight-and-Level Flight and Turns
- ❑ Engine Failure During Descents

INSTRUMENT APPROACHES – ONE ENGINE INOPERATIVE

- ❑ NDB Approach
- ❑ VOR and/or Localizer Approach
- ❑ ILS Approach
- ❑ Approach Procedure to Straight-In Minimums
- ❑ Approach Procedure to Circling Minimums
- ❑ Missed Approach and Holding

INSTRUMENT PROCEDURES

- ❑ VOR Holding
- ❑ NDB Holding
- ❑ VOR Time and Distance
- ❑ Intercepting and Tracking DME Arcs (If Airplane So Equipped)

COMPLETION STANDARDS:

- At the completion of this lesson, the student will be able to identify the inoperative engine during cruise and use the correct control inputs to maintain straight and level flight.
- The student will demonstrate the newly introduced maneuvers and procedures using correct operating techniques, coordination, smoothness, and understanding.
- During engine-out operations, the applicant will be able to make decisions concerning the continued safety of the flight and readily identify the inoperative engine and likely problems.

NOTE: *The day cross-country is complete when the flight has traveled to a point more than 100 nautical miles straight-line distance from the departure point and lasted no less than two hours.*

POSTFLIGHT DISCUSSION AND PREVIEW OF NEXT LESSON

STUDY ASSIGNMENT:

Review, as necessary, the *Multi-Engine Pilot* textbook.

STAGE VII FLIGHT LESSON 9

DUAL — CROSS-COUNTRY, NIGHT CONDITIONS UNDER VFR

RECOMMENDED SEQUENCE:

1. Preflight Orientation
2. Flight
3. Postflight Evaluation

LESSON OBJECTIVES:

- During the lesson, the student will practice the listed review procedures to gain proficiency in basic cross-country instrument flight operations at night.
- Emphasis should be placed on becoming proficient in flying instrument approaches, missed approach procedures, and holding with all engines operating and in engine-out situations.

REVIEW:

CROSS-COUNTRY FLIGHT PLANNING

- ❑ Navigation Systems and Radar Services
- ❑ Pilotage and Dead Reckoning
- ❑ Lost Procedures
- ❑ Diversion
- ❑ Weather Information
- ❑ National Airspace System
- ❑ Aeromedical Factors
- ❑ Radio Communications and ATC Light Signals
- ❑ Airport, Runway, and Taxiway Signs, Markings, and Lighting
- ❑ Lighting and Equipment for Night Flight
- ❑ Physiological Aspects of Night Flight

BASIC INSTRUMENT MANEUVERS

- ❑ Performance Maneuvers (IR)
- ❑ Identification of Inoperative Engine
- ❑ Procedures for Shutdown and Feathering
- ❑ Engine Failure During Climbs

- ❑ Engine Failure During Straight-and-Level Flight and Turns
- ❑ Engine Failure During Descents

INSTRUMENT APPROACHES — ALL ENGINES OPERATING

- ❑ NDB Approach
- ❑ VOR and/or Localizer Approach
- ❑ ILS Approach
- ❑ Missed Approach Considerations

INSTRUMENT APPROACHES — ONE ENGINE INOPERATIVE

- ❑ NDB Approach
- ❑ VOR and/or Localizer Approach
- ❑ ILS Approach
- ❑ Missed Approach Considerations

COMPLETION STANDARDS:

- At the completion of this lesson, the student will be able to identify the inoperative engine during cruise and use the correct control inputs to maintain straight and level flight.
- The student will demonstrate the maneuvers and procedures using correct operating techniques, coordination, smoothness and understanding.

NOTE: *The night cross country is complete when the flight has traveled to a point more than 100 nautical miles straight-line distance from the departure point and lasted no less than two hours.*

POSTFLIGHT DISCUSSION AND PREVIEW OF NEXT LESSON

STUDY ASSIGNMENT:

GROUND LESSON 6 —

Prepare for the Stage VII Check in Flight Lesson 10 and the Stage VI Exam in Ground Lesson 6.

STAGE VII
FLIGHT LESSON 10
DUAL — LOCAL
MULTI-ENGINE STAGE VII CHECK

RECOMMENDED SEQUENCE:

1. Preflight Orientation
2. Flight
3. Postflight Evaluation

LESSON OBJECTIVES:

- The chief instructor, assistant chief, or a designated check instructor will evaluate the student's proficiency in the execution of multi-engine and single-engine operations. The student should be able to execute all maneuvers with positive and smooth aircraft control.

REVIEW:

PREFLIGHT/INFLIGHT

- ❑ Multi-Engine Operations
- ❑ Takeoff, Landing, and Go-Around/Rejected Landing
- ❑ Traffic Pattern
- ❑ Safety-Related Operations and Procedures
- ❑ Systems Management and Awareness

INSTRUMENT APPROACHES — MULTI-ENGINE OPERATIONS

- ❑ NDB Approach
- ❑ VOR and/or Localizer Approach
- ❑ ILS Approach
- ❑ Missed Approach Considerations

INSTRUMENT APPROACHES — ONE ENGINE INOPERATIVE

- ❑ NDB Approach
- ❑ VOR and/or Localizer Approach
- ❑ ILS Approach
- ❑ Missed Approach Considerations

COMPLETION STANDARDS:

- At the completion of this lesson, the student will be able to demonstrate the ability to perform each of the listed maneuvers and procedures at a proficiency level that meets or exceeds those criteria outlined in the multi-engine sections of the current FAA commercial pilot and instrument rating practical test standards.

POSTFLIGHT DISCUSSION AND PREVIEW OF NEXT LESSON

STUDY ASSIGNMENT:

Prepare for the End-of-Course Flight Check in Flight Lesson 11 and the End-of-Course Exam in Ground Lesson 7.

STAGE VII
FLIGHT LESSON 11
DUAL — LOCAL
END-OF-COURSE FLIGHT CHECK FOR COURSE COMPLETION

RECOMMENDED SEQUENCE:

1. Preflight Orientation
2. Flight
3. Postflight Evaluation

LESSON OBJECTIVES:

- The chief instructor, assistant chief, or a designated check instructor will evaluate the student's skills. This is the final stage test in preparation for the Multi-Engine Rating Practical Test.
- The review items may be performed with all engines operating or with one engine inoperative.

REVIEW:

PREFLIGHT PREPARATIONS

- ❑ Certificates and Documents
- ❑ Airworthiness Requirements
- ❑ Multi-Engine Operations of Systems

INFLIGHT MANEUVERS AND PROCEDURES

- ❑ Safety-Related Operations and Procedures
- ❑ Systems Management and Awareness
- ❑ Traffic Pattern
- ❑ Normal Takeoff and Landing
- ❑ Short-Field Takeoff/Maximum Performance Climb and Landing
- ❑ Short-Field Approach and Landing
- ❑ Go-Around/Rejected Landing
- ❑ Straight-and-Level Flight
- ❑ Maneuvering With One Engine Inoperative
- ❑ Constant Altitude Change in Airspeed
- ❑ Constant Airspeed Climbs and Descents
- ❑ Power-Off Stall
- ❑ Power-On Stall
- ❑ Maneuvering During Slow Flight
- ❑ Steep Turns

ENGINE FAILURE

- ❑ Prior to V_{MC}
- ❑ During Straight-and-Level Flight
- ❑ During a Descent

INSTRUMENT APPROACHES — MULTI-ENGINE OPERATIONS

- ❑ NDB Approach
- ❑ VOR and/or Localizer Approach
- ❑ ILS Approach
- ❑ Missed Approach Considerations

INSTRUMENT APPROACHES — ONE ENGINE INOPERATIVE

- ❑ NDB Approach
- ❑ VOR and/or Localizer Approach
- ❑ ILS Approach
- ❑ Missed Approach Considerations

INSTRUMENT PROCEDURES

- ❑ VOR Holding
- ❑ NDB Holding
- ❑ VOR Time and Distance
- ❑ Intercepting and Tracking DME Arcs (If Airplane So Equipped)
- ❑ Approach Procedures to Circling Minimums
- ❑ Approach Procedures to Straight-In Minimums
- ❑ Missed Approach Procedures
- ❑ Cross-Country Planning

EMERGENCY PROCEDURES

- ❑ Emergency Descent
- ❑ Systems and Equipment Malfunction
- ❑ Emergency Equipment and Survival Gear

POSTFLIGHT PROCEDURES

- ❏ After Landing
- ❏ Parking and Securing

COMPLETION STANDARDS:

- The student will perform all VFR, IFR, and pertinent simulated emergency procedures at the proficiency level, as outlined in the current FAA Multi-Engine Commercial Pilot and Instrument Rating Practical Test Standards.

POSTFLIGHT DISCUSSION AND PREVIEW OF NEXT LESSON

This is to certify that

____

is enrolled in the
Federal Aviation Administration

approved ______________________ course

conducted by ____________________.

______________________ ______________________
Date of Enrollment Chief Instructor

This is to certify that

____

is enrolled in the
Federal Aviation Administration

approved ______________________ course

conducted by ____________________.

______________________ ______________________
Date of Enrollment Chief Instructor

This is to certify that

____

is enrolled in the
Federal Aviation Administration

approved ____________________________ course

conducted by ______________________.

Date of Enrollment ________________

Chief Instructor ________________

This is to certify that

____

has successfully completed all stages, tests, and course requirements and has graduated from the FEDERAL AVIATION ADMINISTRATION

approved ____________________________ course

conducted by ____________________________.

The graduate has completed the cross-country training specified in FAR Part 141.

- ❑ Instrument Rating Course — Appendix C, Paragraph 4(c)(1)(ii)
- ❑ Commercial Pilot Certification Course — Appendix D, Paragraphs 4 and 5
- ❑ Multi-Engine Course — Appendix I, Paragraph 4

I certify the above statements are true.

____
Chief Instructor

____
School Certificate Number

____
Date of Graduation

This is to certify that

____

has successfully completed all stages, tests, and course requirements and has graduated from the FEDERAL AVIATION ADMINISTRATION approved ____________________ course conducted by ____________________.

The graduate has completed the cross-country training specified in FAR Part 141.

- ❑ Instrument Rating Course — Appendix C, Paragraph 4(c)(1)(ii)
- ❑ Commercial Pilot Certification Course — Appendix D, Paragraphs 4 and 5
- ❑ Multi-Engine Rating Course — Appendix I, Paragraph 4

I certify the above statements are true.

____

Chief Instructor

____

School Certificate Number

____

Date of Graduation

This is to certify that

____

has successfully completed all stages, tests, and course requirements and has graduated from the FEDERAL AVIATION ADMINISTRATION approved ____________________ course conducted by ____________________.

The graduate has completed the cross-country training specified in FAR Part 141.

- ❑ Instrument Rating Course — Appendix C, Paragraph 4(c)(1)(ii)
- ❑ Commercial Pilot Certification Course — Appendix D, Paragraphs 4 and 5
- ❑ Multi-Engine Rating Course — Appendix I, Paragraph 4

I certify the above statements are true.

____

Chief Instructor

____

School Certificate Number

____

Date of Graduation